My Treasury of
STORIES and
RHYMES

© 2004 by Parragon Books Ltd

This 2008 edition published by Barnes & Noble, Inc.,
by arrangement with Parragon.

Barnes & Noble, Inc.
122 Fifth Avenue
New York, NY 10011

ISBN 13: 978-1-4351-0440-2
ISBN-10: 1-4351-0440-4

Printed and bound in Indonesia
1 3 5 7 9 10 8 6 4 2

Every effort has been made to acknowledge the contributors to this book.
If we have made any errors, we will be pleased to rectify them in future editions.

My Treasury of
STORIES and
RHYMES

Bath New York Singapore Hong Kong Cologne Delhi Melbourne

Contents

Millie the Mixed-Up Mail Carrier

Millie the Mail Carrier worked hard delivering letters, and she was always in a hurry. She hated to keep the people on her round waiting—and Mr Price the Postmaster always expected her back at the mail office by 12 o'clock.

One morning Millie was in a bigger hurry than ever. She had overslept and was late for work! "Hurry, hurry, rush and hurry!" Millie muttered to herself as she rushed out the door.

"People are waiting for their mail!" Millie the Mail Carrier said to herself, as she sped to the mail office on her bike. "And Mr Price will be waiting for me!" She zoomed down the street as fast as she could go.

"Sorry I'm late, Mr Price," Millie puffed as she flew through the mail office door.

"Good morning, Millie!" said Mr Price. "Your mailbag is all ready—and it looks very full today!"

"Thanks, Mr Price," said Millie. "I'll really have to hurry, with all those letters and parcels!"

Millie sped down Main Street and tore around the corner of Jackson Road. She was going so fast that she didn't see the removal truck in front of her until it was too late! "LOOK OUT!" shouted the removal men. "Oh dear!" shouted Millie, as she flew off her bike. Everything in Millie's mailbag went flying, too!

"Oh no! It will take ages to collect all these!" cried Millie, when she had stood up and dusted herself off, "and I'm in such a hurry today!"

The removal men helped Millie collect all the letters, postcards and parcels and put them back in her bag. It wasn't too long before she was ready to go.

But when Millie picked up her bike, she saw that the tire was flat! "I've got a puncture!" she cried. "I can't ride this now. What will I do?"

"You'll have to walk your round today, Millie," said one of the removal men.

"Oh no!" said Millie. "I'm late enough as it is! I'd better get going!" Millie ran off to deliver the mail as quickly as she could.

But she was in such a hurry that she got all the names and addresses mixed up!

Mr Green, on Jackson Road, was expecting a parcel of books. Instead, he got two letters and a power bill addressed to Mrs Jackson!

Mrs Jackson, who lived on Holly Drive, got a magazine that was supposed to go to Holly Walker!

And Holly Walker, who lived on Green Street, got the parcel of books meant for Mr Green!

Everybody was terribly confused, especially Millie the Mail Carrier!

"I must be going mad!" she exclaimed.

Millie rushed and hurried as quickly as she could to try and sort everything out... but by 11 o'clock her mailbag was still half full.

She was beginning to feel hopeless, when suddenly she saw something that gave her a great idea.

"Jack, may I borrow your skateboard, please?" Millie asked one of the children. "I promise to return it as soon as I've delivered all my mail."

"Sure, Millie," said Jack.

Millie had never been on a skateboard before, but she bravely stepped on. Millie wibbled and wobbled... and teetered and tottered... then she skidded and swayed... and WHOOOOSHED and WHIZZZED down the street.

"Wheeeeeeeee!" cried Millie with glee. "This is just what I need!"

Millie zoomed up and down the street at lightning speed. She had such a good time that the rest of her round seemed to get done very quickly.

"This is much faster than walking," she said, "and much more fun than my bike!"

At last Millie's deliveries were done. She returned the skateboard to Jack, and had just enough time to rush back to the mail office.

"I'm back, Mr Price!" she gasped, tripping over her bike as she staggered through the door. "Right on time!"

"I'm glad, Millie," said Mr Price. "And I'm glad you're all right. The removal men brought back your bike. I guess we'll have to mend that puncture right away."

"Oh there's no hurry, Mr Price," said Millie. "I've found a much better form of transport for a mixed-up mail carrier like me!"

Bella Bunny's Bonnet

In pretty Primrose Wood, there was great excitement. It was the Spring Parade. All the animals were joining in because a prize was being given for the best bonnet. "I bet I'll win," said Bella, who was a very vain bunny. "What can I use for my hat?" she wondered, as she skipped through the woods. Bella gathered some pretty Spring flowers, then called her friend, Binky the pigeon, for help. The friends worked hard, weaving daffodils and bluebells into a beautiful display.

"There," said Binky, "perfect." Bella put on the pretty hat and smiled.

"I know I'm going to win!" she cried. Binky just smiled. Bella really was the vainest animal in Primrose Wood! At last, it was time for the parade. The animals from Folly Farm were all wearing jolly bonnets. "There isn't one hat as pretty as mine," giggled Bella. "It looks good enough to eat!" Gordy the goat thought so, too. Trotting behind Bella, he nibbled her bonnet, until he had gobbled up nearly all the flowers!

Then, Holly the horse gave a loud neigh. "The winner of this year's parade is Felicity the fox!" she said.

Everyone cheered—except Bella. "But mine is the best—look!" Bella took the hat off her head. "Aaagghh! My lovely hat!" she cried, looking at a clump of twigs!

"Oops!" said Gordy. "Sorry, Bella."

"But you have won something," sniggered Holly. "The prize for the funniest hat!"

Brave Billy Bunny

At the edge of Frog Pond Wood, there lived a friendly, little bunny called Billy, his brother Bobby and lots of bunny friends. The one thing Billy really, really hated was getting wet! One sunny day, the other bunnies and Bobby hopped off to the stream, to play. "Come on, Billy!" they called.

"No way!" cried Billy. "I hate the water!"

What Billy loved doing most of all was running. So, while the other bunnies played at the stream, Billy ran through the wood, leaping over logs and weaving in and out of the trees—he was very fast! Suddenly, Bouncer Bunny came rushing back from the stream.

"Billy! Come quickly!" he panted. "Bobby's fallen into the water and is being washed away!" Billy rushed off towards the stream, leaving poor Bouncer far behind. When Billy reached the stream, he could just see his little brother, Bobby, splashing away in the rushing water.

"Help!" cried Bobby. "I can't swim!"

Then, Billy began to run! He managed to get ahead of Bobby. Quickly, Billy jumped into the water, swam up to his brother and, coughing and spluttering, dragged poor Bobby to the side.

"Billy!" cried the others. "You're a hero!"

"A wet hero!" said Billy, grinning. "Getting wet wasn't so bad after all. I'm going for another swim!"

Barney the Boastful Bear

Barney was a very boastful bear. "Look at my lovely soft fur!" he would say to the other toys. "See how it shines!"

Barney loved to talk about himself. "I'm the smartest toy in the playroom!" he would say. "It's a well-known fact."

He didn't know that the other toys all laughed about him behind his back.

"That bear thinks he's so smart," growled Scotty Dog. "But he isn't smart enough to know when everyone's fed up with him!"

"He'll learn his lesson one of these days," said Molly Monkey, and sure enough, that is just what happened...

One hot summer's day, the toys lazed in the warm playroom. "Wouldn't it be lovely if we could all go for a walk outside," said Rag Doll.

"We could have a lovely picnic in the woods!" said Old Bear.

"Even better, we could all go for a drive in the toy car first!" said Rabbit.

"But none of us is big or smart enough to drive the toy car," said Rag Doll, sadly.

"I am!" came a voice from the corner. It was Barney. He had been listening to them talking.

"I can drive the toy car. And I know the best place for a picnic in the woods," he said.

"We've never seen you drive the car," said Rabbit, suspiciously.

"That's because I drive it at night, when you're asleep," said Barney. "I'm a very good driver, in fact."

"Ooh, let's go then!" cried Rag Doll. And in no time they had packed up a picnic and were sitting ready in the car.

"Er, I don't feel like driving today, actually," mumbled Barney. "It's too hot." But the others were not interested in hearing excuses, so rather reluctantly Barney climbed into the driver's seat and started the engine. You see, the truth was, Barney had never really driven the car before, and he was scared. But he wanted to show off, so he pretended to know what he was doing.

Off they set down the garden path. "Toot, toot!" Barney beeped the horn as he turned the little car out into the country lane, and soon they were driving along, singing merrily.

All was going well, until Rag Doll suddenly said, "Hey, Barney, didn't we just miss the turning for the woods?"

"I know where I'm going," said Barney, crossly. "Leave it to me." And he made the little car go faster.

"Slow down a bit, Barney!" called Old Bear, from the back seat. "My fur is getting all ruffled." He was starting to feel anxious.

"I don't need a back-seat driver, thank you," said Barney, with a growl, and made the car go even faster. By now the others were starting to feel scared, but Barney was having a great time.

"Aren't I a wonderful driver!" he chuckled. "Look—no hands!" And he took his paws off the steering wheel. Just then they reached

a sharp corner. The little car went spinning off the side of the road and crashed into a tree, tipping all the toys out into the ditch!

They were a bit dazed, but luckily no one was hurt. They were not pleased with Barney though.

"You're a silly bear!" said Rabbit, crossly. "We could all have been badly hurt!"

"We'll have to walk home now," said Rag Doll, rubbing her head. "Where are we?"

Everyone looked at Barney.

"Don't ask me!" he said, quietly.

"But you told us that you knew the way!" said Old Bear, indignantly.

"I was only pretending," said Barney,

his voice trembling. "I don't really know how to drive, and I don't know where we are!" And he started to cry.

The other toys were furious with Barney.

"You naughty boastful bear!" they scolded. "Now see what trouble your boasting has got us into!"

The lost toys walked through the dark woods all night long, clinging together in fright as shadows loomed around them.

They had never been out at night before. Then just before dawn, they spotted the little house where they lived, and crept back into the playroom.

What a relief it was to be home again!

Luckily their owner had not noticed they were missing, so she never knew what an adventure her toys had been having while she was fast asleep. She often wondered what had happened to her toy car though.

Whale Song

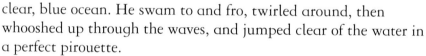

"**O**h, what a beautiful morning!" sang Flippy, the whale, as streaks of sunlight filtered down through the clear, blue ocean. He swam to and fro, twirled around, then whooshed up through the waves, and jumped clear of the water in a perfect pirouette.

Flippy loved to sing and dance. The trouble was, although he was a very graceful dancer, his singing was terrible. His big mouth would open wide, as he boomed out song after song—but none of them were in tune! The dreadful sound echoed through the ocean for miles, sending all the fish and other ocean creatures diving into the rocks and reefs for cover, as the waters shook around them. It was always worse when the sun shone, as the bright warm sun made Flippy want to sing and dance with happiness. It had got so bad that the other creatures had begun to pray for dull skies and rain.

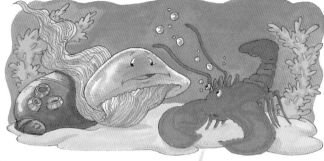

"Something has got to be done!" complained Wobble, the jellyfish. "Flippy's booming voice makes me quiver and shake so much that I can't see where I'm going!"

"Well, I know where I'm going," said Snappy, the lobster. "As far away as possible. My head is splitting from Flippy's awful wailing."

"Someone will have to tell Flippy not to sing any more," said Sparky, the stingray.

"But it will hurt his feelings," said Wobble.

"Not as much as his singing hurts my ears!" snapped Snappy.

And so they decided that Sparky would tell Flippy the next day that they did not want him to sing any more songs. Wobble was right. Flippy was very upset when he heard that the others did not like his singing. He cried big, salty tears.

"I was only trying to enjoy myself!" he sobbed. "I didn't realise I was upsetting everyone else."

"There, there," said Sparky, wishing he had not been chosen to give the little whale the bad news. "You can still enjoy dancing."

"It's not the same without music," said Flippy, miserably. "You can't get the rhythm." And he swam off into the deep waters, saying he wanted to be alone for a while.

As Flippy lay on the bottom of the ocean floor, feeling very sorry for himself, a beautiful sound came floating through the water from far away in the distance. It sounded like someone singing. Flippy wanted to know who was making such a lovely sound so, with a flick of his big tail, he set off in the direction it was coming from.

As he got closer, he could hear a soft voice singing a beautiful melody. Peering out from behind a big rock, he saw that the voice belonged to a little octopus, who was shuffling and swaying about on the ocean floor. His legs seemed to be going in all directions, as he stumbled and tripped along. Then he tried to spin around, but his legs got tangled and he crashed to the ground in a heap.

"Oh, dear," said Leggy, the octopus. "I seem to have eight left feet!"

Flippy looked out shyly from behind the rock.

"What are you trying to do?" he asked.

The little octopus looked rather embarrassed.

"I was trying to dance," he said, blushing pink. "Only I'm not very good at it."

"Well, maybe I could teach you," said Flippy. "I'm a very good dancer. And then, in return, there is something that I would love you to teach me!"

A few weeks later, Wobble, Snappy and Sparky were discussing how they missed having Flippy around, when they heard a strange and beautiful sound floating towards them through the ocean.

"Oh, what a beautiful morning..." came the song, only this time there were two voices singing in perfect harmony!

"Surely that can't be Flippy!" said the others in surprise. But to their amazement, as the voices came closer they saw that, sure enough, it was Flippy, spinning and twirling as he danced gracefully towards them with his new friend!

Harvey the Shyest Rabbit

Harvey the rabbit was the shyest animal in the glade beside Looking-Glass Pond. He was too shy to talk to anyone... too shy to play with the other animals... too shy even to look out from behind his big floppy ears.

"There's no need to be scared," Mama Rabbit told him. "If you want to join in, all you have to do is ask."

But Harvey just hid behind the long grass. No one even noticed that he was there!

One morning, Harvey was sitting beside Looking-Glass Pond—alone, as usual.

"I wish I could make a friend," he sighed. "But how can I, when no one even notices me?"

Harvey gazed down sadly at the pond. He could hardly believe his eyes! There in the water was another little rabbit with big floppy ears, staring back at him.

"He looks just as scared as me!" thought Harvey. He waved shyly at the rabbit in the water. The water rabbit waved too! Harvey did a bunny hop in surprise. The water rabbit did a bunny hop. "Hello!" said Harvey bravely, smiling.

"Hello!" said the rabbit, smiling back. "So that's how you make friends!" cried Harvey, in amazement. "You just need to be a little bit brave."

He was so excited, he forgot all about being shy or scared. Instead, he raced off to tell everyone the good news.

And this time, everyone noticed him! Soon Harvey had lots of new friends to play with. But he never forgot to visit his very first friend in Looking-Glass Pond!

Intery, Mintery Cutery, Corn

Intery, mintery, cutery, corn,
  Apple seed and apple thorn.
Wire, briar, limber, lock,
  Three geese in a flock.

One flew east and one flew west;
  One flew over the cuckoo's nest.

Once I Saw a Little Bird

Once I saw a little bird
  Come hop, hop, hop;
So I cried, "Little bird,
  Will you stop, stop, stop?"
And was going to the window,
  To say, "How do you do?"
But he shook his little tail,
  And far away he flew.

Little Robin Redbreast

Little Robin Redbreast
  Sat upon a rail:
Niddle-noddle went his head!
  Wiggle-waggle went his tail.

The North Wind doth Blow

The north wind doth blow,
  And we shall have snow,
And what will poor Robin do then?
  Poor thing!

He'll sit in a barn,
  And to keep himself warm,
Will hide his head under his wing.
  Poor thing!

Jay-bird

Jay-bird, jay-bird, settin' on a rail,
  Pickin' his teeth with the end of his tail;
Mulberry leaves and calico sleeves—
  All school teachers are hard to please.

Two Little Dicky Birds

Two little dicky birds sitting on a wall,
One named Peter, one named Paul.
  Fly away, Peter!
  Fly away, Paul!
    Come back, Peter!
    Come back, Paul!

The Cuckoo

Cuckoo, Cuckoo,
  What do you do?
In April
  I open my bill;
In May
  I sing night and day;
In June
  I change my tune;
In July
  Away I fly;
In August
  Away I must.

Magpies

One for sorrow, two for joy,
  Three for a girl, four for a boy,
Five for silver, six for gold,
  Seven for a secret never to be told.

Greedy Bear

If there is one thing in the whole wide world that a teddy bear likes more than anything, it is buns—big sticky currant buns with sugary tops, and squishy middles. A teddy bear will do almost anything for a bun. But for one greedy little teddy bear called Clarence, sticky buns were to be his unsticking!

Rag Doll baked the most wonderful buns in the little toy cooker. She baked big buns and small buns, iced buns and currant buns, jam buns and cream buns, and even hot-cross buns! She shared them out amongst the toys in the playroom, and everybody loved them. But no one loved them as much as Clarence.

"If you will give me your bun, I'll polish your boots!" he'd say to Tin Soldier.

And sometimes, if Tin Soldier was not feeling too hungry, he'd agree. There was always someone who would give Clarence their bun in return for a favor, and sometimes Clarence would eat five or six buns in one day!

Then he'd be busy washing the dolls' dresses, brushing Scotty Dog's fur, or cleaning the toy policeman's car. He would even stand still and let the clown throw custard pies at him!

So you see, Clarence was not a lazy bear, but he was a greedy bear, and in spite of all his busyness, he was becoming a rather plump little greedy bear. All those buns were starting to show around his middle, and his fur was beginning to strain at the seams!

Then one day Clarence rushed into the playroom full of excitement. His owner, Penny, had told him that next week she was taking him on a teddy bears' picnic.

"She says there will be honey sandwiches and ice-cream and cookies—

and lots and lots of buns!" Clarence told the others, rubbing his paws together. "I can hardly wait! In fact all this excitement has made me hungry, so I think I'll have a bun." And he took a big sticky bun out from under a cushion where he'd hidden it earlier.

"Oh, Clarence!" said Rabbit. "One of these days you will simply go pop!"

"Just be happy I don't like carrots!" said Clarence, with a smile.

Well, that week Clarence was busier than ever. Every time he thought about the picnic he felt hungry, and then he'd have to find someone who'd let him have their bun. He ate bun after bun, and would not listen

when Rag Doll warned him that his back seam was starting to come undone.

The day of the teddy bears' picnic dawned, and Clarence yawned and stretched, smiling with excitement. But as he stretched he felt a popping sensation all down his stomach. He tried to sit up in bed, but to his alarm he found he could not move. He looked down to see that the seams around his tummy had popped open, and his stuffing was spilling out all over the bed!

"Help!" he cried. "I'm exploding!"

Just then, Penny woke up. "Oh, Clarence!" she cried when she saw him. "I can't take you to the teddy bears' picnic like that!"

Penny showed Clarence to her mommy, who said he would have to go to the toy hospital.

Clarence was away from the playroom for a whole week, but when he came back he was as good as new. Some of his stuffing had been taken out, and he was all sewn up again.

He had had lots of time to think in the hospital about what a silly greedy bear he had been. How he wished he had not missed the picnic. The other teddies said it was the best day out they had ever had. Penny had taken Rabbit instead.

"It was terrible," moaned Rabbit. "Not a carrot in sight. I did save you a bun though." And he pulled a big sticky bun out of his pocket.

"No thank you, Rabbit," said Clarence. "I've gone off buns!"

Of course, Clarence did not stop eating buns for long, but from then on he stuck to one a day. And he still did favors for the others, only now he did them for free!

A Swarm of Bees in May

A swarm of bees in May
  Is worth a load of hay;
A swarm of bees in June
  Is worth a silver spoon;
A swarm of bees in July
  Is not worth a fly.

Bow, Wow, Wow

Bow, wow, wow,
  Whose dog art thou?
"Little Tom Tinker's dog,
  Bow, wow, wow."

Itsy Bitsy Spider

Itsy Bitsy Spider
  Climbing up the spout;
Down came the rain
  And washed the spider out.
Out came the sunshine
  And dried up all the rain;
Itsy Bitsy Spider
  Climbing up again.

Tinker, Tailor

Tinker, tailor,
  Soldier, soldier,
Rich man, poor man,
  Beggarman, thief!

The Cold Old House

I know a house, and a cold old house,
  A cold old house by the sea.
If I were a mouse in that cold old house
  What a cold, cold mouse I'd be!

Hickory, Dickory, Dock

Hickory, dickory, dock,
  The mouse ran up the clock.
The clock struck one,
  The mouse ran down,
Hickory, dickory, dock.

Bat, Bat

Bat, Bat, come under my hat,
  And I'll give you a slice of bacon,
And when I bake I'll give you a cake,
  If I am not mistaken.

Three Blind Mice

Three blind mice, three blind mice!
  See how they run, see how they run!
They all ran after the farmer's wife,
  Who cut off their tails with a carving-knife,
Did ever you see such a thing in your life,
  As three blind mice?

One Stormy Night

It was Patch's first night outside in his smart new doghouse. He snuggled down on his warm blanket and watched as the skies grew dark. Before long, he fell fast asleep. As he slept, big spots of rain began to fall. A splash of water dripped from the doghouse roof on to his nose.

Just then, there was a great crash and a bright flash of light lit up the sky. Patch woke with a start and was on his feet at once, growling and snarling. "It's just a silly old storm," he told himself. "Nothing to scare a fearless farm dog like me!" But as the lightning flashed again, he saw a great shadow looming against the barn. Patch gulped. Whatever could it be? Patch began to bark furiously, trying to act braver than he felt. Next time the lightning flashed, there was no sign of the shadow. "I soon scared that monster away!" he thought.

But as Patch settled back down in his cozy bed, the sky outside lit up once more, and there in the doorway towered the monster!

"Just checking you're okay in the storm," said Mommy, giving Patch a lick on the ear.

"A fearless farm dog like me?" said Patch. "Of course I am!" But as the storm raged on, he snuggled up close to her all the same!

The Cow who Jumped over the Moon

Boing, boing, boing! Bouncy Bunny kicked up her heels and bounded happily across the field.

"I can bounce high in the air, watch me!" she called to the other animals on the farm. Her fluffy white tail bobbed up and down.

"Very good!" said Silly Sheep, who was easily impressed.

"Yes, very good," said Swift, the sheepdog. "But not as good as me. I can jump right over the gate." With that, he leapt over the gate and into the field.

"Amazing!" said Silly Sheep.

"Yes, amazing," said Harry Horse, with a flick of his mane. "But not as amazing as me. I can jump right over that hedge. Watch me!" And with that, he galloped around the field, then leapt high into the air, and sailed over the tall hedge.

"Unbelievable!" said Silly Sheep.

"Yes, unbelievable," said Daisy, the cow, chewing lazily on a clump of grass. "But not as unbelievable as me. I can jump right over the moon!"

"Well, I'm afraid that is unbelievable, Daisy," said Harry Horse. "No one can jump over the moon. That's just a fairy story."

"Well, I can," said Daisy, stubbornly. "And I can prove it! You can watch me do it if you like!"

The other animals all agreed that they would very much like to see Daisy jump over the moon.

"Meet me here in the field tonight, then," said Daisy to them. "When the moon is full, and the stars are shining bright."

So that night, when the moon had risen high up in the sky, the excited animals gathered together in the field. The rest of the animals from the farm came along too, for word had soon spread that Daisy, the cow, was going to jump over the moon, and they were all eager to watch.

"Come along then, Daisy," said Swift, the farm dog, as the animals waited impatiently. "Are you going to show us how you can jump over the moon, or not?"

All the animals laughed because they thought that Daisy was just boasting, and that she would not really be able to do it.

"Yes, I am going to show you," said Daisy, "but, first of all, you will have to come with me. This isn't the right spot." Daisy led the animals across the field, to the far side, where a little stream ran along the edge of the field, separating it from the dark woods on the other side. As they crossed the field, they looked up at the great, yellow moon shining down on them. It looked so very far away. However did Daisy think that she could jump so high?

"Now, stand back everyone, and give me some room," said Daisy. The animals did as they were asked, and watched Daisy with anticipation, giggling nervously. Whatever was she going to do?

Daisy trotted back to the middle of the field, turned, then stopped, shuffling backwards and forwards as she took up her starting position.

"Come on, Daisy," cried the animals, impatiently. Daisy took a deep breath, then ran towards the stream at a great speed.

At the last moment, she sprang into the air, and sailed across the stream, landing safely on the other side.

"I did it!" cried Daisy. "Aren't you going to clap, then?" The other animals looked at each other in confusion.

"But you only jumped over the stream!" said Harry Horse, puzzled.

"Come and take a closer look," called Daisy, still on the far side. The animals gathered close to the water's edge. They looked down, and there reflected in the water, shimmered the great full moon! How the animals laughed when they realised Daisy had tricked them.

"See?" said Daisy. "I really can jump over the moon!" And just to prove it, she jumped back to the field again. The animals all clapped and cheered.

"That was a very good trick!" said Swift, the farm dog.

"Amazing!" said Silly Sheep. "Could someone explain it to me again, please!"

Katy and the Butterfly

As Katy Kitten lay dozing happily in the sun, something tickled her nose. She opened an eye and saw a butterfly hovering above her whiskers, but as she tapped at it with her soft paw it fluttered away. Katy sprang after the butterfly, missed it and landed with a howl in a bed of thistles. "I'll catch that butterfly!" she said, crossly.

Katy chased the butterfly towards the stream, where it settled on the branch of a tree. She climbed after it, high into the tree, but every time she came near, the butterfly simply flew away—and by now, she was stuck! Nervously, she looked down at the stream swirling below her.

Just then, the butterfly fluttered past her nose. Without thinking, Katy swiped at it with her paw. But as she did so, she lost her balance and went tumbling down through the tree, landing with a great SPLASH! in the water below. "Help!" cried Katy, waving her paws wildly.

Luckily she caught hold of a branch hanging over the stream and clambered onto the bank.

Katy arrived home, cold and wet. She curled up, exhausted, in front of the fire, but just as she started to doze, she felt something tugging at her whiskers. She opened one eye and saw a little mouse.

"Oh no, I've done enough chasing for one day, thank you!" said Katy.

Fred the Fearless Fireman

Fireman Fred hurried to the fire station. It was his turn to cook lunch for the firemen on his shift, and he had just bought some nice, plump sausages at the butcher's.

At the fire station, Fred bumped into Builder Benny, who had come to repair a broken window frame.

"Oops! Hello, Benny!" he said. Then he went straight to the kitchen to start cooking. The smell of sausages wafted through the fire station. "Mmm, those sausages smell good!" said Dan and Mike, the other firemen, as they arrived for work. Suddenly the alarm bell rang—
CLANG! CLANG! CLANG!

"Emergency!" cried Fireman Mike. He and Fireman Dan rushed down the pole and into their fire-fighting gear. "What about the sausages?" cried Fireman Fred.

"Don't worry about a thing," said Builder Benny, coming in through the window. "I'll look after them till you get back."

"Thanks, Benny!" said Fireman Fred, trying to get his apron off as he rushed down to join the others. The emergency was in Tony's Pizza

Parlor. One of the ovens had caught fire!

"We'll have that blaze out in a flash!" said Fred, rushing in with a big fire extinguisher. Dan and Mike followed with the hose.

With a WHIIISH! and a WHOOOSH! from Fred, and a SPLIISH! and a SPLOOOSH! from Mike and Dan, the fire was soon out.

"WHOOPS!" cried Fireman Fred, slipping on the wet floor. But he was back on his feet in a flash. "Thank you!" said Tony, as the firemen took their equipment back to the truck. "I can get back to baking pizzas now!"

Just when they were ready to go back to the station, the firemen heard a call coming through over their radio. "Emergency! Emergency! Window cleaner in distress on Pine Avenue. Emergency! Over…"

"We're on our way!" said Fireman Fred, starting the engine. "Over and out!"

NEE-NAW! NEE-NAW! With sirens blaring, the fire truck zoomed into Pine Avenue. A crowd had gathered around Tip-Top Towers, the tallest building in town.

"It's Will the window cleaner!" cried Millie the Mail Carrier, who had just finished delivering the day's mail to the building. "His ladder has broken, and he's hurt his leg. Now he's stuck, and he can't get down! Can you help him?"

"Certainly!" said Fireman Fred. "I can be up there in no time!"

The firemen put up their tallest ladder. While Mike and Dan held out a net—just in case—Fred fearlessly began scrambling up the ladder. "Here I come, Will!" he shouted.

"I've got you!" said Fred, as he grabbed hold of the window cleaner. The crowd below cheered as Fred carried Will down the ladder and helped him into the fire truck.

Fred drove the fire truck straight to the hospital.

"Thank you for rescuing me," Will said to Fred.

"Don't mention it," said Fred. "I'm sure your leg will be fine—but I think you'll need a new ladder!"

"What a busy day it's been!" said Fireman Fred, as they drove back to the fire station. "I feel really frazzled!"

"Our work's not over yet!" said Fireman Dan. "Look! There's smoke up ahead! NEE-NAW! NEE-NAW! went the siren.

VRROOOM! VRROOOM! went the engine, as it raced to the scene of the fire.

The smoke was coming from the fire station! Dan and Mike unwound the hose, and Fred raced inside. "Oooof!" he gasped, as he tripped over the hose and bumped into Benny—again!

"Sorry, guys," said a red-faced Builder Benny. "I guess I burnt the sausages. I think your lunch is ruined."

Poor Fred felt really frazzled now— until he had an idea. "I know just the person to rescue us from this situation!" he said.

"Who?" asked the others. "Tony!" said Fireman Fred.

"His pizzas are yummy, and an extra-large one will be a perfect lunch for all of us!"

I Love Little Pussy

I love little pussy, her coat is so warm;
And if I don't hurt her she'll do me no harm.
So I'll not pull her tail nor drive her away,
But pussy and I very gently will play.

Pussycat Mole

Pussycat Mole,
  Jumped over a coal,
And in her best petticoat
  burnt a great hole.
Poor pussy's weeping,
  she'll have no more milk,
Until her best petticoat's
  mended with silk.

Pussycat, Pussycat

Pussycat, pussycat, where
  have you been?
I've been to London to visit
  the Queen.
Pussycat, pussycat, what
  did you there?
I frightened a little mouse
  under her chair.

Pussycat Sits by the Fire

Pussycat sits by the fire.
  How did she come there?
In walks the little dog,
  Says, "Pussy! are you there?
How do you do, Mistress Pussy?
  Mistress Pussy, how d'ye do?"
"I thank you kindly, little dog,
  I fare as well as you!"

Mary had a Little Lamb

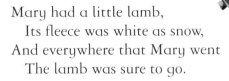

Mary had a little lamb,
  Its fleece was white as snow,
And everywhere that Mary went
  The lamb was sure to go.

It followed her to school one day,
  Which was against the rule;
It made the children laugh and play
  To see a lamb in school.

Frisky Lamb

A frisky lamb
  And a frisky child
Playing their pranks
  In a cowslip meadow:
The sky all blue
  And the air all mild
And the fields all sun
  And the lanes half-shadow.

Baa, Baa, Black Sheep

Baa, baa, black sheep, have you any wool?
  Yes, sir, yes, sir, three bags full;
One for the master, one for the dame,
  And one for the little boy that lives down the lane.

On the Grassy Banks

On the grassy banks
  Lambkins at their pranks;
Woolly sisters, woolly brothers,
  Jumping off their feet,
While their woolly mothers
  Watch them and bleat.

The Princess and the Pea

Once upon a time, there was a prince whose dearest wish was to marry a princess—but only a true princess would do. In order to find her, he traveled far and wide, all over the land.

He met young princesses and old ones, beautiful princesses and plain ones, rich princesses and poor ones, but there was always something that was not quite right with each of them.

The prince began to despair. He called together his courtiers and announced, "I have failed to find my dream princess. We will go home to our palace without delay."

One dark night, back at his palace, there was the most tremendous storm. Lightning flashed across the sky and thunder buffeted the thick palace walls.

The prince and his parents were talking in the drawing room. He was telling them all about his hopeless search for a perfect princess to marry. "Don't despair, dear," said his mother, the queen. "Who knows what surprises the future may hold. You could find your perfect princess when you least expect to."

Just then, they heard a tiny tap-tapping at the window. The prince opened it, and standing there before him was a very beautiful, but very wet, young lady. Her hair was dripping, her dress was soaked through, and she was shivering with cold.

"I am a princess," she told the prince, "and I am lost. Please may I come in and shelter from the storm?"

The prince was astonished. He asked the girl into the palace, then he turned to the queen and whispered in her ear, "Oh, Mother, she is enchanting! But how can I be sure she really is a princess?"

"Leave it to me," said his mother, and she hurried off to have a bedroom prepared for the pretty girl.

First, the queen placed a little green pea on the mattress. Then she ordered the servants to bring twenty thick mattresses, and twenty feather quilts, which they piled on top of the pea. The princess needed a very tall ladder to climb into bed that night!

The next morning, at breakfast, the queen asked the princess if she had slept well.

"I had the most awful night!" said the princess. "I don't know what it was, but there was a hard lump under my bed, and it kept me awake all night, and now I'm absolutely covered with bruises!"

"At last!" the queen exclaimed, "our search is over! We have found a true princess for our son. Only a real princess would have

skin so tender that she could feel a pea through twenty mattresses and twenty feather quilts!"

The prince was overjoyed, and he and the princess were soon married.

As for the little green pea, the prince had a special cabinet made and it was put on display in the royal museum, where it can still be seen today!

Witches on the Run

At night, when it's all dark and scary, as you peek out over the bed covers, you might see shapes on the wall that will give you a fright! The thought of witches high on the ceiling, with broomsticks, pointed hats and capes can keep you awake all night.

If you think about it for too long, it just gets worse—you can hear their ear-piercing cackles and screams, and the bubbling of their cauldron. If you look really hard, you can see the cauldron glowing with a strange light as the witches cast their spells. They stir the dreadful mixture with a huge wooden spoon, adding slimy green bits. And as you lie there shaking, the smell from the spell gets stronger and the bubbling gets louder!

But there is one thing on the planet that all real witches hate, and that is anything that is clean, particularly clean children! Of course witches never wash, and the thought of children with clean skin makes them feel very ill. They much prefer to be smelly and grimy.

So, the next time you think there are witches flying on your ceiling, remember all you need is clean skin and they will vanish as quick as a flash!

Lonely Hearts

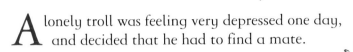

A lonely troll was feeling very depressed one day, and decided that he had to find a mate.

Although this was a good idea, it gave the troll a problem—where does a troll go to find a mate? After thinking for ages he decided the best thing to do was to advertise for someone in the local paper. This is what he wrote:

Fun-loving troll, dirty and smelly,
  With damp slimy skin and big hairy belly
Nice muddy fingers and grubby wet toes,
  Hot steamy breath and rings through each nose.
With stains on his shirt and holes in his socks,
  Teeth that need cleaning and knots in his locks,
Tears in his pants and scuffs on his shoe.
  He's waiting to meet someone lovely like you.
He likes dirty ditches and hiding in holes,
  Is certain to win when he fights other trolls.
Is very attentive, will woo you with roses,
  After he's used them to pick both his noses!
He lives on his own, in a dark stinking pit,
  Oozing with slime and covered in spit.
Now feeling lonely, he hopes there's a chance
  He can meet someone similar for fun and romance!

Do you know anyone who will reply?

Rumpelstiltskin

Once upon a time there was a boastful miller. One day, he told the king that his daughter was so clever that she could spin gold out of straw.

"I must meet this remarkable girl," said the king. "Bring her to the palace at once."

The king took the miller's daughter to a room filled with straw. In one corner stood a spinning wheel. "You must spin all this straw into gold before morning," the king told the girl, "or you will be put to death." Then he went out and locked the door behind him.

The poor girl sat at the spinning wheel and wept. However could she make gold from straw? Suddenly, the door flew open, and in leapt a funny-looking little man.

"Why are you crying?" he asked.

When the girl told him what the king had said, the strange man replied, "What will you give me if I spin this straw into gold for you?"

"My pearl necklace," said the girl.

So the little man sat down at the spinning wheel and quickly spun all the straw into gold. Then he magically vanished from the room.

The next morning, the king was amazed at all the gold—but now he wanted even more. He took the girl to a bigger room, and had it filled with straw. Once again, he told her to spin the straw into gold by morning, or she would die. Then he left.

The poor girl sat down and wept. Suddenly, the odd little man appeared. "What will you give me if I help you this time?" he asked.

"My pretty ring," the girl replied.

So the little man began to spin, and soon all the straw had been turned into gold. Then he vanished.

The next morning the greedy king was astounded but still not satisfied. He took the girl to an even bigger room, piled to the ceiling with straw. "If you succeed this time, you will become queen," the king said. "If you

fail, you know what will happen."

As soon as the girl was alone, the little man appeared. "I have nothing left to give you," said the girl.

"Then promise me your first-born child when you become queen," said the man.

"I might never become queen and I may never have a child," the girl thought, and so she promised.

So the strange little man sat down at the spinning wheel and began to work. He spun for many hours and the pile of gold grew higher and higher.

"At last," said the little man, "my task is done." Then he vanished. The girl gazed around the room. It was stacked from floor to ceiling with glistening gold that shone like the sun.

At dawn, the king was overjoyed. He kept his promise and soon married the miller's daughter.

The whole kingdom rejoiced, and the king and his new queen were very happy together.

A year later, the king and queen had a baby. By this time, the queen had forgotten all about her promise—but the funny little man had not. One night, he appeared in the queen's bedroom. "I have come for your baby!" he announced gleefully.

"No!" cried the queen. "I will give you jewels, gold, anything you wish! But please do not take my baby." She wept so miserably that the little man took pity on her.

"Very well," he said. "If you can guess my name within three nights you may keep your baby. If not, the child is mine!" Then he disappeared.

The queen sent messengers out to gather names from every town and village in the kingdom. They returned with thousands of suggestions. Over the next two evenings, when the little man arrived, the queen questioned him again and again:

"Is your name Tom?"

"No," replied the strange little man.

"Jack? Dick? Peter?" she asked. The strange man shook his head. "Could it be Brutus or Clarence, then?"

Each time, the reply was the same: "No, Your Majesty."

By the third day, only one messenger had not returned. Late that afternoon, he was on his way back to the palace when he saw a hut in a forest clearing. In front of it, an odd little man was dancing around a fire, singing:

"I'll be the winner of this game!
The queen will never guess my name!
She will lose, and I will win,
Because my name is…
Rumpelstiltskin!"

The messenger galloped back to the palace and told the queen what he had seen and heard. She was so grateful that she rewarded the messenger with a huge sack of gold.

That night, the queen eagerly waited in her throne room for the little man. When he appeared, the queen asked, "Is your name Guzzletum?"

"No, it's not!" laughed the little man.

"Is it Bumblebottom? Jigglejoggle? Tickletooth or Wigglewoggle?"

"No! No!" he cackled. "Your time's running out, Your Majesty!"

The queen smiled. "Could it be… Rumpelstiltskin?"

The little man could not believe his ears and flew into a rage. "Who told you? Who told you?" he shrieked. "How did you find out?"

He cried and squealed and beat the floor with his fists.

"You've won! You've won!" he wailed, and disappeared in a shower of sparks.

The little man never came back to worry the queen again, and they all lived happily ever after.

Home Sweet Home

Bella Bunny looked at the sweet, green grass growing in the pasture on the far side of the stream. She was tired of eating the rough grass that grew near her burrow. "I'm going to cross the stream!" she said to her brothers and sisters, pointing to a fallen branch that lay across it.

Bella bounced safely across the branch and was soon eating the sweet, juicy grass on the other side of the stream. Her brothers and sisters thought she was very brave and wondered if they should follow. But just then, they saw a sly fox creeping up behind Bella through the grass!

"Look out!" they called.

Bella turned to see the fox just in time! She leapt back onto the branch, but she was in such a hurry that she slipped and fell into the stream. Luckily, Becky Beaver had been watching and she pulled Bella safely to the other side.

"Home sweet home!" gasped Bella, with relief. And she ran off to join her brothers and sisters, vowing never to leave home again.

Benny the Barmy Builder

Benny was a hard-working builder, and he always did his very best. But sometimes he could be forgetful!

One morning, Benny the Builder arrived bright and early at Vicky Vet's surgery. "Benny the Builder at your service!" he announced. "I think you have a job for me to do."

"Not me, Benny," replied Vicky. "But Millie the Mail Carrier has!"

"Of course!" said Benny. "Sorry—I really shouldn't be so forgetful!"

And off he went to Millie the Mail Carrier's house. "Benny the Builder at your service!" Benny announced. "Woof!" said Benny's dog, Rocky.

"Come in," called Millie.

She took out a drawing to show Benny.

"I want you to build a playhouse in my garden," Millie said. "It's a surprise for my grandchildren, Peter, Penny and Patty. I did this drawing to show

you just how it should look."

Benny and Millie looked at the drawing together.

"The playhouse should have two tall doors," said Millie, "one at the front and one at the back, with one small step at the back door. There should be five windows, one at either side of the front door and one on each of the other sides."

"Yes, I see," said Benny.

"And I want a nice sloping roof," said Millie, "not a flat roof!"

"Yes, I see," said Benny. "I will do my very best!"

Millie left for the mail office, and Benny went out to start work. But he had barely begun when a gust of wind came along. WHOOSH! went Millie's drawing, up in the air. "WOOF!" barked Rocky, leaping up to catch it.

Oh no! The drawing got caught in the branches of a tree!

Rocky leapt as high as he could and snatched down the drawing, but, by the time he got it back, it was in shreds.

"Oh dear!" moaned Benny the Builder. "How will I build the playhouse now?"

Benny tried to remember everything in the drawing. But he quickly got very confused!

"Was it five windows and two doors with one step?" Benny puzzled. "Or was it two windows and five doors with three steps? Was the roof flat and not sloping? Or sloping and not flat? Were the doors tall or small? Oh dear, oh dear!"

Benny decided that he would just have to do the best he could. He got to work measuring… mixing… laying bricks… sawing wood… hammering nails… fixing screws… plastering and painting… and doing his very best to make everything just right.

Late that afternoon, Millie the Mail Carrier got home from work. She couldn't wait to see what Benny had done. But, what a surprise she had! The Wendy house's roof was flat. The bottom of the house was sloping. There were two steps leading up to two doors on one side of the house and there were two floors, both different sizes. And there were two windows on one side of the house.

"It's all wrong!" said Millie to Benny. "How will you ever fix it in time?"

But Benny didn't have a chance to answer because, just at that moment, Millie's grandchildren arrived.

"Oooh! Look! A playhouse!" they cried happily as they rushed towards it. "There's a door for each of us!" they all cried together.

"And we can climb right up to the roof!" said Patty.

"And slide down the other side!" said Peter.

"And there are loads of windows so it's nice and bright inside!" said Penny.

"Granny, it's the best playhouse ever!" the children told Millie. "It is perfect. Thank you so much!"

"Well, I think you should thank Benny the Builder," said Millie , smiling. Benny the Builder smiled too. "I just did my very best," he said.

The New Cat

The cats on Old MacDonald's farm like nothing better than dozing. Milly just loves to laze in the sun, and Lazy, as his name suggests, hardly opens his eyes!

One day, Milly was snoozing on a bale of hay, when she heard Old MacDonald talking on the telephone through the open kitchen window. Half-asleep, she heard him say, "The new cat…" Milly was feeling very sleepy. "Yes," continued Old MacDonald, "I need it because the ones I have now are useless."

Milly yawned and stretched, still drowsy and happy. Then she suddenly sat bolt upright. What? The cats were useless? A new one was coming? Oh no!

Milly dashed to where Lazy was fast asleep and eventually woke him up! She hurriedly shouted what she had heard.

"What's the matter with us?" yawned Lazy in a hurt voice. "I don't understand."

"You don't do anything," clucked Henrietta the hen, who liked to put her beak into everybody's business. "You just sleep all day."

Milly and Lazy looked at each other. They knew there was only one thing to do. Ten seconds later, they were rushing around the farmyard, trying to look as busy as possible!

By the end of a week of dashing around all day and miaowing all night, the cats had created quite a stir in the farmyard.

"Look here," said Bruce the farm dog. "What has got into you both?"

Milly and Lazy explained. Bruce tried not to smile. "Well, you're doing the right thing," he barked. "Impress Old MacDonald like this and you'll be fine. But I would stop the caterwauling at night."

Bruce strolled off chuckling to himself. As Old MacDonald's right-hand dog, he knew that the farmer was waiting for a new CATalogue to order his winter wellies from. But he didn't think he needed to tell Milly and Lazy that—not quite yet anyway!

Bear Feels Sick

Teddy Bear came home from school feeling tired and sick. "I don't want my hot chocolate," he told Mommy Bear. Teddy Bear sat on the couch and closed his eyes. "And I don't want to watch television either," he said.

"Do you want to play your drum?" asked Mommy Bear, looking worried. Teddy Bear shook his head, so Mommy Bear went to fetch the thermometer and she put it under Teddy Bear's tongue. "Oh dear," she said. "I'm afraid you're a very sick Teddy Bear. Up to bed you go!"

The next morning Teddy Bear was covered all over in bright red spots. "Look at me!" he said proudly, showing off his belly.

"You've got chicken pox," said Mommy Bear. "You'll have to stay home from school today."

"Yippee!" said Teddy Bear. But he said it quietly, because his head was quite sore. Teddy Bear lay on the couch all day, watching television and coloring some pictures. Mommy Bear read him stories and brought him soup and ice-cream to eat.

After a few days the spots disappeared.

"Can I play my drum?" asked Teddy Bear. Mommy Bear was so glad to see Teddy Bear looking well again, that she let him play his drum for the rest of the afternoon.

Hungry
Bear

"I'm hungry!" said Teddy Bear.

"You've just finished your lunch," said Mommy Bear. "You can have something in a little while."

"But I want something now!" wailed Teddy Bear. "I'm starving!"

"If you eat any more you'll go pop!" said Mommy Bear.

"I only want a cookie! Or ice-cream. Or maybe a piece of cake. I'm really hungry!" grumbled Teddy Bear. He went outside and made hungry faces through the window.

"You don't look hungry," said Betty Bear from next door.

"I am!" said Teddy Bear. Nobody else came by, so Teddy Bear climbed into his sandpit. He dug some roads and built a few houses. He built a huge castle on a hill, with a moat around it. Then he fetched some water from the faucet and filled the moat.

"Teddy!" called Mommy Bear. "You can come inside now and have some cakes!"

But Teddy Bear just shook his head— he was having far too much fun to feel hungry any more!

Little Dog Lost

"**B**rrr," shivered Scruffy. "It's cold tonight."

"Well, snuggle up closer to me," said his mom.

"It's not fair," Scruffy grumbled. "Why do we have to sleep outside in the cold? The cats are allowed to sleep inside, and they have nice warm baskets!"

"We're farm dogs, dear," said Mom. "We have to be tough, and work hard to earn our keep."

"I'd rather be a cat," mumbled Scruffy. "All they do is wash themselves, eat and sleep."

"We don't have such a bad life," said Mom. "Now stop feeling sorry for yourself, and get some rest. We've got a lot of work to do tomorrow."

The next day, Scruffy woke early and trotted down the lane for a walk. He ran through the grass, chasing rabbits, and sniffing at the flowers.

Now, usually when he got to the end of the lane he stopped and turned back. But today, he saw a big red truck parked outside a house there. The back of the truck was open, and Scruffy thought he would just climb inside and take a look.

The truck was full of furniture. At the back was a big armchair with soft cushions. Scruffy clambered onto it. "I could doze all day, like a cat!" he told himself. He closed his eyes and before he knew it he had fallen fast asleep.

Scruffy awoke some time later with a sharp jolt.

"Oh, no, I fell asleep!" he groaned. "I'd better hurry back. We've got a busy day ahead!"

But then he saw that the truck doors were closed! He could hear voices talking outside.

"Oh, dear, I'll be in trouble if I get found in here," thought Scruffy, and he hid behind the chair.

The back of the truck opened and Scruffy peered out. Two men started unloading the furniture.

When Scruffy was sure that no one was looking, he crept out of the truck, but he was no longer in the countryside where he lived! He was in a big noisy town, full of buildings and cars.

Poor Scruffy had no idea where he was!

"The truck must have carried me away," thought Scruffy, feeling very frightened.

All day long, Scruffy roamed around trying to find his way home, feeling cold, tired, and hungry. At last, he lay down and began to howl miserably.

"What's the matter, pup?" he heard a man's kind voice say. "You look lost. Come home with me." Scruffy gave the man's hand a grateful lick, then jumped up and followed him home.

When they arrived at the man's house Scruffy sat on the doorstep, hoping the man might bring out some food for him to eat. But the man said, "Come in, you can't stay out there."

Scruffy followed the man in, and found a little poodle waiting to meet him. Scruffy stared at her in amazement. What ever had happened to her fur?

"You'd better take a bath before supper," said the man, looking at Scruffy's dirty white coat. The man washed him in a big tub, then brushed his tangled coat. Scruffy howled miserably. What had he done to deserve such punishment?

"Don't you like it?" asked the poodle, shyly.

"No, I don't," said Scruffy. "I think that all this washing and cleaning is for cats!"

Next the man gave them supper—small bowls of dry pellets. Scruffy looked at them and sniffed in disgust. He was used to chunks of meat and a nice big bone.

"This looks like cat food," said Scruffy, miserably.

After supper the poodle climbed into a big basket in the kitchen.

"I thought that belonged to a cat," said Scruffy. He tried sleeping in the basket but he was hot and uncomfortable. He missed counting the stars to help him fall asleep, but most of all he missed his mom.

"I want to go home," he cried, and big tears slipped down his nose.

The next day, the man put Scruffy on a lead and took him into town. He hated the way he was dragged along, without being able to stop and have a good sniff at things.

Then, as they crossed the market place, Scruffy heard a familiar bark, and saw his mom's head hanging through the window of the farmer's truck, parked by the side of the road! He started to howl, dragged the man over to the truck, then he leapt up at the window and barked excitedly. The farmer could hardly believe that this little dog was Scruffy—he had never seen him so clean! The man explained how he had found Scruffy, and the farmer thanked the man for taking such good care of him.

Scruffy and his mother leapt into the back of the truck. On the way back home, Scruffy told his mom all about his adventure and what had happened.

"I thought you must have run away because you didn't like being a farm dog," she said gently.

"Oh, no, Mom," said Scruffy, quickly. "I love being a farm dog. I can't wait to get home to a nice big juicy bone and our little bed beneath the stars!"

Webster the Littlest Frog

Webster was the littlest frog on the pond, and he was fed up. Fed up with being bossed about. Fed up with playing on his own. Fed up, in fact, with being the littlest frog. None of the bigger frogs would let Webster play games with them.

"Hop it, Titch!" they croaked. "You're far too small to join in our games."

Every day, Webster sat on his own, watching the other frogs play leap-frog on Looking-Glass Pond.

"You don't have to be a big frog to jump," thought Webster, as he watched. "I can do that."

At last, one bright, moonlit evening Webster found the courage to ask the other frogs if he could join in.

"Please let me play with you," said Webster. "I can jump really high!"

The other frogs just laughed.

"But I can!" he insisted. He took a deep breath. "I can jump... over the moon!"

The other frogs laughed so much, they nearly fell off their lily pads.

"I'll prove it!" he said. "Just watch me."

One... two... three JUMP! Webster leapt off his lily pad and sailed over the moon's reflection in the pond.

The other frogs stared in amazement. It was true. Webster could jump over the moon!

"We're sorry we didn't believe you," said one of the big frogs.

"Of course you can play with us. You might not be the biggest frog on the pond, but you certainly are the smartest!"

Tiggy-Touchwood

Tiggy-tiggy-touchwood,
my black hen,
She lays eggs for gentlemen.
Sometimes nine and sometimes ten,
Tiggy-tiggy-touchwood,
my black hen.

I had a Little Hen

I had a little hen, the prettiest ever seen,
She washed me the dishes, and kept the house clean;
She went to the mill to fetch me some flour,
She brought it home in less than an hour;
She baked me my bread, she brewed me my ale,
She sat by the fire and told many a fine tale.

Mrs Hen

Chook, chook, chook, chook, chook,
Good morning, Mrs Hen.
How many chickens have you got?
Madam, I've got ten.

Four of them are yellow,
And four of them are brown,
And two of them are speckled red,
The nicest in the town.

I had a Little Cow

I had a little cow;
   Hey-diddle, ho-diddle!
I had a little cow, and it had a little calf;
   Hey-diddle, ho-diddle; and there's my song half.

I had a little cow;
   Hey-diddle, ho-diddle!
I had a little cow, and I drove it to the stall;
   Hey-diddle, ho-diddle; and there's my song all!

The Shortest Tongue Twister

Peggy Babcock

Little Boy Blue

Little Boy Blue,
   Come blow your horn,
The sheep's in the meadow,
   The cow's in the corn.

Where is the boy
   Who looks after the sheep?
He's under a haycock
   Fast asleep.
      Will you wake him?
      No, not I,
      For if I do,
      He's sure to cry.

Princess Petal

Princess Petal lives in a shiny white castle surrounded by beautiful grounds, filled with pretty flowers and colorful butterflies. The Princess's best friend is Sparkle, a sweet little puppy. Every morning, he helps the princess to chose her dress.

"Which one today?" she asks.

Sparkle stands next to a pretty yellow one, wags his tail and barks.

"Perfect," says the Princess.

Then they play games in the grounds. They love to run and jump and play "catch the ball."

Princess Petal

Today, Princess Petal is very excited. She has just received an invitation to a special party —a ball at the palace.

"The Prince is very handsome," Petal says to her puppy. "I must look my best."

She slips on a beautiful pink dress, trimmed with jewels and satin ribbons. On her feet are dainty gold slippers. Then Petal opens her jewelery box and takes out a pair of crystal earrings and a diamond tiara.

She places the tiara carefully on her head—now she can go off to the ball in her beautiful horse-drawn carriage.

As the Princess and Sparkle enter the crowded ballroom, everyone gasps in delight. The handsome Prince takes the Princess's hand.

"You are the loveliest lady here," he says. "May I have this dance?"

"Of course, Your Majesty!" says the Princess.

Princess Petal is the happiest girl in the whole kingdom.

Lazy Teddy

There was nothing Lazy Teddy liked more than to be tucked up snug and warm in Joshua's bed.

Every morning the alarm clock would ring and Joshua would leap out of bed and fling open the curtains. "I love mornings!" he'd say, stretching his arms up high as the sun poured in through the window. "You're crazy!" Teddy would mutter, and he'd burrow down beneath the quilt to the bottom of the bed, where he'd spend the rest of the morning snoozing happily.

"Come out and play, you lazy bear," Joshua would call. But Lazy Teddy wouldn't budge. He would just snore even louder.

Joshua wished that Teddy would be more lively, like his other friends' bears. He loved having adventures, but they would be even better if Teddy would share them with him.

One evening, Joshua decided to have a talk with Teddy before they went to bed. He told him about the fishing trip he'd been on that day with his friends and their teddy bears.

LAZY TEDDY

"It was lots of fun, Teddy. I wish you'd been there. It really is time you stopped being such a lazybones. Tomorrow is my birthday, and I'm having a party. There will be games, and presents and ice-cream. Please promise you'll come?"

"It does sound like fun," said Teddy. "Okay, I promise. I'll get up just this once."

The next morning, Joshua was up bright and early. "Yippee, it's my birthday today!" he yelled, dancing around the room. He pulled the covers off his bed. "Come on, Teddy, time to get up!"

"Just five more minutes!" groaned Teddy, and he rolled over and fell straight back to sleep. When Joshua came back up to his room after breakfast, Teddy still wasn't up. Well, by now Joshua was getting quite cross with Teddy. He reached over and poked him in the tummy. Teddy opened one eye and growled. "Wake up, Teddy! You promised, remember?" said Joshua.

Teddy yawned. "Oh, if I must!" he said, and muttering and grumbling he climbed out of bed. He washed his face and

paws, brushed his teeth and put on his best red vest.

"There, I'm ready!" he said.

"Good," said Joshua. "About time too!"

Just then the doorbell rang, and Joshua ran to answer it. "I'll come and fetch you in a minute," he said to Teddy. But when he returned there was no sign of Teddy, just a gentle snoring coming from the bottom of the bed.

Joshua was so cross and upset with Lazy Teddy, that he decided to leave him right where he was.

"He'll just have to miss the party!" he said. Deep down though, he was hurt that Teddy wouldn't keep his promise.

Joshua enjoyed his party, although he wished that Teddy had been there. Later that night when he got into bed, he lay crying quietly into his pillow.

LAZY TEDDY

Teddy lay awake in the dark, listening. He knew Joshua was crying because he had let him down, and he felt very ashamed.

"I'm sorry!" whispered Lazy Teddy, and he snuggled up to Joshua and stroked him with a paw until he fell asleep.

The next morning when the alarm clock rang, Joshua leapt out of bed, as usual. But what was this? Teddy had leapt out of bed too, and was stretching his paws up high. Joshua looked at him in amazement.

"What are we doing today, then?" asked Teddy.

"G...g...going for a picnic," stammered Joshua, in surprise. "Are you coming?"

"Of course," said Teddy. And from that day on, Teddy was up bright and early every day, ready to enjoy another day of adventures with Joshua, and he never let him down again.

Moo! Moo! Moo!

The Meadow Ladies Chorus,
Is something rather new.
You'll hear them all too clearly,
They're singing, "Moo! Moo! Moo!"

They try to trill like budgies,
And copy blackbirds, too.
The only song they really know,
Of course, is, "Moo! Moo! Moo!"

They practise in the morning,
And in the night-time, too.
It doesn't make a difference though,
They still sing, "Moo! Moo! Moo!"

You Need a Cow!

How does fresh milk reach your shake,
The frothy, creamy kind you make?
You ask how?—You need a cow!
How does butter reach your bread,
The slithery, slippery stuff you spread?
You ask how?—You need a cow!
How does your cheese reach your plate,
The yummy, yellow kind you grate?
You ask how?—You need a cow!
How does ice cream reach your spoon
The kind you cannot eat too soon?
You ask how?—You need a cow!

Counting Sheep

Old MacDonald's counting sheep,
But not because he cannot sleep.
You see, he's wondering if maybe,
Each sheep has now had her baby.
"Stand still!" he cries. "Be still and steady,
I might have counted you already!"
Poor Old MacDonald's feeling dizzy!
Then suddenly he starts to smile.
"Goodbye! I'll see you in a while."
When all the farm is soundly sleeping,
Old MacDonald's softly creeping.
It's really easy to count sheep,
When you're awake and they're asleep!

Wooly Coats

In the middle of the winter,
All the animals complain,
"Our furry coats are much too thin.
They let the icy north wind in.
We want to go indoors again!"
But while the rest all shiver,
Sheep are fine and look quite smug,
"We will not come to any harm.
We are the warmest on the farm.
Our wooly coats will keep us snug!"

Clip, Clop!

Pigs can prance,
    And ducks can dance,
Hens flutter in a flurry.
    But George plods on and doesn't stop,
Clip, clop! Clip, clop!
    He's *never* in a hurry.

"Of course, I know
    My horse is slow,
But I will never worry.
    For George plods on and doesn't stop,
Clip, clop! Clip, clop!
    He doesn't *need* to hurry."

Egg Hatching Dream

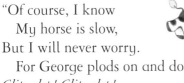

When Jenny is sitting,
    And sitting, and sitting,
She can't take up knitting,
    Or sew a fine seam.

If her eggs are to hatch,
    Every one of the batch,
There is nothing to match,
    An egg-hatching dream.

Her thoughts travel far and near.
    Half-asleep she'll appear,
Until she starts to hear,
    Her eggs start to crack!

A Horse, of Course!

Who can you trust when the
    tractor breaks down,
And the nearest mechanic is
    off in the town?
Who is as big and as strong as a horse?
    Oh, silly me, a horse, of course!
Who do you know who can eat
    tons of hay,
And even munch ten sacks of oats
    in a day?
Who has an appetite large as a horse?
    Oh, silly me, a horse, of course!
Who will stick by you when you
    need a friend,
And hear all your troubles right through
    to the end?
Who is as wise and as kind as a horse?
    Oh, silly me, a horse, of course!

One Hen Pecking

One hen pecking in the garden—
    Mrs MacDonald shakes her head.
Two hens pecking in the garden—
    Makes her shake her fist instead!
Three hens pecking in the garden—
    The farmer's wife comes storming out.
Four hens pecking in the garden—
    Mrs MacDonald starts to shout.

89

Vicky the Very Silly Vet

"**G**ood morning!" calls Vicky Vet as she opens the door to her surgery. "How are all my animals today?"

Vicky starts her early morning rounds with Goldie the Goldfish. Vicky Vet loves looking after animals but sometimes she gets very mixed up! She knows she has a busy morning ahead of her, so Vicky wants to get all the cages cleaned, and the animals fed, before her first patient arrives. I'll give you some clean newspaper first, Patch," she says to the messy puppy, "and then I'll give your blanket a good shake, Tabby."

"There you are, Tabby. A nice fluffy bed for you," says Vicky, putting the blanket back into Tabby's basket, when… Brriiing, brriiing! Brriiing, brriiing! "That's the phone, Tabby," she cries.

Vicky Vet drops everything and rushes to answer it. "Now, where was I?" thinks Vicky Vet to herself, coming back to the cages.

"I was just about to give you some fresh wood chips, wasn't I?" she says to Hickory and Dickory, the two mice. Just as she is putting the wood chips in the mouse cage…

Ding dong! goes the doorbell. "Who can that be?" Vicky wonders.

"My first patient's not due for half an hour!" Vicky hasn't noticed that the cage doors are open and Patch is busy chasing Tabby around the room!

It is Millie the Mail Carrier with a parcel that is too big to fit through the letterbox. "Thank you, Millie," says Vicky, "but I don't think this parcel is for me. It's addressed to Tony's Pizza Parlour."

"Oh dear!" says Millie. "How could I be so mixed-up? Sorry, Vicky!"

"Now," says Vicky Vet, "I think I was about to clean Percy Parrot's cage." She has just finished cleaning the cage when she feels something scampering up her leg!

"Oh no!" cries Vicky. "Hickory and Dickory, how did you escape? "And Patch and Tabby! How did you get out?" Very silly Vicky is flapping about trying to catch all the animals, and all the time Percy is hopping closer to the open door of his cage. Vicky dives at Tabby and pounces on Hickory and Dickory and is busy chasing Patch back into his cage when… SUDDENLY there is a loud squawk! Percy Parrot is flying towards the open window!

"Wait! Percy! Stop!" she cries, rushing after the parrot. Luckily, Vicky catches Percy just in time. Once he is safely back in his cage, she manages to round up Hickory and Dickory, get Tabby back into her basket, and shut Patch safely into his cage.

"Phew!" she puffs. "I feel as if I've done a whole morning's work already. "I think after all this, it must be time for some breakfast!"

Vicky lines up the feeding bowls and animal feed on the table. Carefully, she measures out some delicious dog food for Patch and gives him a big juicy bone to chew. Then she spoons out some crunchy bird seed for Percy, some fishy cat food for Tabby, and some tasty sunflower seeds for the mice. Vicky has nearly finished making breakfast for the animals when… Ding dong! It's the doorbell again.

"Oh!" she cries. "My first patient is here already! I'd better hurry!" As quickly as she can, Vicky puts the food bowls in the cages—but she doesn't look to see who is getting what! So Patch the dog gets a bowl of crunchy bird seed. Hickory and Dickory the mice get the dog food and the big juicy bone. Tabby the cat gets the tasty sunflower seeds. And Percy the parrot gets the fishy cat food! What's more, Vicky is in such a rush that she leaves all the cage doors open again!

This time, though, the animals know just what to do. Hickory and Dickory find their sunflower seeds in Tabby's basket. Tabby discovers her fishy cat food in Percy's cage.

Percy pecks at his bird seed in Patch's cage. And Patch finds his delicious dog food in the mouse cage.

Fred Fireman is at the door with his dog Dot for a check-up.

"Come in," says Vicky Vet. "You're right on time."

"We always like coming here," says Fireman Fred. "The animals are so happy and everything seems so relaxed. What's your secret, Vicky?"

Very silly Vicky thinks about her crazy morning and wonders what dreadful mess will greet Fred as they walk into the surgery. But clever Patch, Tabby, Percy and the mice are back in their own cages. Vicky sees the clean and tidy room and grins at her animals.

"Treats for tea," she whispers!

One Bad Bunny

Barney was a very bad bunny. He liked playing tricks on his friends. Barney hid Squirrel's nut store and it took him all day to find it. He put sticky honey on Badger's walking stick and Badger was chased by bees. And he put black paint on Mole's glasses, so poor Mole got even more lost than usual!

"It's time we taught that bad bunny a lesson!" said Badger, crossly. So that night, while Barney was sleeping, Mole and Badger dug a big hole. Squirrel climbed up to the treetops and fetched some branches to put over the hole and they covered it with grass. They set a big juicy carrot on top, then hid behind the trees to wait.

The next morning, Barney came bouncing out of his burrow, spotted the juicy carrot and jumped straight into the trap!

"Help!" he cried, from the bottom of the hole. The others appeared.

"We tricked you!" they laughed. They only let Barney out when he promised to stop playing tricks on them. And from then on he was a very good bunny indeed.

The Fly

Little Fly,
 Thy summer's play
My thoughtless hand
 Has brushed away.

Am not I
 A fly like thee?
Or art not thou
 A man like me?

For I dance,
 And drink, and sing,
Till some blind hand
 Shall brush my wing.

If thought is life
 And strength and breath,
And the want
 Of thought is death;

Then am I
 A happy fly,
If I live
 Or if I die.

WILLIAM BLAKE

Aiken Drum

There was a man lived in the moon,
 and his name was Aiken Drum
And he played upon a ladle,
 and his name was Aiken Drum.

And his hat was made of good cream cheese,
 and his name was Aiken Drum.

And his coat was made of good roast beef,
 and his name was Aiken Drum.

And his buttons were made of penny loaves,
 and his name was Aiken Drum.

His waistcoat was made of crust of pies,
 and his name was Aiken Drum.

His breeches were made of haggis bags,
 and his name was Aiken Drum.
And he played upon a ladle,
 and his name was Aiken Drum.

Ladybug! Ladybug!

Ladybug! Ladybug! Fly away home,
 Night is approaching, and sunset is come.
The herons are flown to their trees by the Hall;
 Felt, but unseen, the damp dewdrops fall.
This is the close of a still summer day;
 Ladybug! Ladybug! haste! fly away!

EMILY BRONTË

Three Wise Old Women

Three wise old women were they, were they,
  Who went to walk on a winter day:
One carried a basket to hold some berries,
  One carried a ladder to climb for cherries,
The third, and she was the wisest one,
  Carried a fan to keep off the sun.

But they went so far, and they went so fast,
  They quite forgot their way at last,
So one of the wise women cried in a fright,
  "Suppose we should meet a bear tonight!
Suppose he should eat me!"
  "And me!!" "And me!!!"
"What is to be done?" cried all the three.

Whether they ever sailed home again,
  Whether they saw any bears, or no,
You must find out, for I don't know.

The Kangaroo

Old Jumpety-Bumpety-Hop-and-Go-One
  Was lying asleep on his side in the sun.
This old kangaroo, he was whisking the flies
  (With his long glossy tail)
    from his ears and his eyes.
Jumpety-Bumpety-Hop-and-Go-One
  Was lying asleep on his side in the sun,
Jumpety-Bumpety-Hop!

Ducks' Ditty

All along the backwater,
  Through the rushes tall,
Ducks are a-dabbling.
  Up tails all!

Ducks' tails, drakes' tails,
  Yellow feet a-quiver,
Yellow bills all out of sight
  Busy in the river!

Slushy green undergrowth
  Where the roach swim—
Here we keep our larder,
  Cool and full and dim.

Every one for what he likes!
  We like to be
Heads down, tails up,
  Dabbling free!

High in the blue above
  Swifts whirl and call—
We are down a-dabbling
  Up tails all!

Mrs Mouse's Vacation

Mrs Mouse was very excited. All year she had been so busy. First there had been nuts and berries to gather in readiness for winter. Then she had needed to give her little house a big spring clean to make it nice and fresh. Now, as the warm sun shone down on the trees and flowers of her woodland home, she had promised herself a well-deserved vacation. But getting ready for vacations seemed to make one busier than ever! There was so much to do!

First she took out her little case, opened it and placed it carefully on her neatly made bed. Then she rushed to her cupboard and selected some fine vacation clothes. Back to her case she scuttled and laid them in. Now she chose several pairs of shoes—a nice pair of sandals for walking along the front in, a pair of smart shoes for shopping in, an even smarter pair for going to dinner in, and another pair just in case!

"I'll need a couple of sun hats," she thought to herself, and so into the case they went as well. These were followed by a coat, some gloves and a scarf (just in case the breeze got up and it became cold). Then, in case it became very sunny, in went some sunglasses, some sun cream and a sunshade. But, oh dear, there were so many things in the case that it refused to shut. She tried sitting on it, and bouncing on it, but still it stubbornly would not close.

So out from the case came all the things that she had just put in, and Mrs Mouse scurried to the closet again and chose an even bigger case. This time they all fitted perfectly, and she shut the case with a big sigh of relief.

Now she was ready to go to the beach for her vacation. She sat on the train, with her case on the rack above her head, munching her hazelnut sandwiches and looking eagerly out of the window hoping to see the sea. Finally, as the train chuffed around a bend, there it was! A great, deep blue sea shimmering in the sun, with white gulls soaring over the cliffs and headlands.

"I'm really looking forward to a nice, quiet rest," she said to herself.

Her guesthouse was very comfortable, and so close to the sea that she could smell the clean, salty air whenever she opened her window. "This is the life," she thought. "Nice and peaceful."

After she had put her clothes away, she put on her little swimsuit and her sun hat and packed her beach bag. Now she was ready for some peaceful sunbathing!

At the beach, she found herself a quiet spot, closed her eyes and was soon fast asleep. But not for long! A family of voles had arrived on the beach, and they weren't trying to have a quiet time at all. The youngsters in the family yelled at the top of their voices, splashed water everywhere, and sent their beach ball tumbling all over Mrs Mouse's neatly laid out beach towel.

Just as Mrs Mouse thought that it couldn't get any noisier, along came a crowd of ferrets. Now if you've ever sat on a beach next to a crowd of ferrets, you'll know what it's like. Their noisy shouting and singing made Mrs Mouse's head buzz.

Mrs Mouse couldn't stand it a moment longer. She was just wondering where she might find some peace and quiet when she spotted a rock just a little way out to sea.

"If I swim out to that rock," she thought, "I will surely have some peace and quiet there." She gathered up her belongings and swam over to the rock. It was a bit lumpy, but at least it was quiet. Soon she was fast asleep again.

Just then the rock started to move slowly out to sea! It wasn't really a rock at all, you see, but a turtle which had been dozing near the surface. Off into the sunset it went, with Mrs Mouse dozing on its back, quite unaware of what was happening.

Eventually, the turtle came to a deserted island. At that moment, Mrs Mouse woke up. She looked at the empty beach, and, without even knowing she had been sleeping on a turtle, she jumped off and swam to the shore, thinking it was the beach that she had just left.

Just then, the turtle swam off, and Mrs Mouse suddenly realised what had happened. For a moment she was horrified. But then she looked at the quiet, palm-fringed beach with no one about but herself, and thought of the noisy beach she had just left.

"Well, perhaps this isn't such a bad place to spend a quiet vacation after all," she thought.

And that's just what she did. Day after day she lazed on her own private beach with no one to disturb her. There were plenty of coconuts and fruits to eat, and she wanted for nothing. She even made herself a cozy bed from palm leaves.

Eventually, though, she started to miss her own little house in the woods and decided it was time to get back home. First she took half a coconut and nibbled out the tasty inside. "That will make a fine boat to sit in," she said.

Next she found a palm leaf and stuck it in the bottom of the shell. She took her little boat to the water's edge and, as the wind caught her palm leaf sail, off she floated back to the boarding house to get her belongings. As she sailed slowly back she thought, "This is the quietest vacation I've ever had. I may come back here next year!"

I Love my Puppy

I love my puppy because he wags his tail and comes to meet me.

He barks and jumps in the air when he wants to play, and chases my big bouncy ball.

He fetches a stick for me to throw.

He scampers beside me when we go for walks in the park.

But I love him most when he is sleepy and we snuggle up close.

I Love my Kitten

I love my kitten because she purrs softly when I stroke her.

She pounces on a ball of wool and rolls it between her paws.

She runs along the garden wall and leaps over the gate.

She washes her face by licking her soft padded paws.

She peeps through the cat flap to see if her dinner is ready.

But I love her most of all when she sits with her tail curled all around her.

I Love my Pony

I love my pony because he neighs hello when I come to visit him.

He lets me sponge him and brush his soft shiny mane.

He eats a shiny green apple right out of my hand.

He's fun to be with when we go for long rides.

He jumps at the show and wins a bright red rosette.

But I love him most of all when I talk to him and he nuzzles up close.

I Love my Bunny

I love my bunny because he twitches his nose, and has smooth silky fur.

Bunny nibbles a carrot with his bright white teeth.

He runs in the garden and his fluffy white tail bobs up and down.

He digs a hole in the lawn with his big soft paws.

He sits quietly as I stroke his big floppy ears, and his whiskers twitch up and down.

But I love him most when he dozes off to sleep sitting on my lap.

Crocodile Smiles

"Say cheese!" said the photographer.
"CHEESE!" grinned Snappy, the crocodile. Lights flashed, and cameras clicked as he gave his most winning smile.

"You're a natural!" cried the expedition leader. He was with a team of wildlife photographers. Snappy smiled at his reflection in the river.

"Ooh, you are a handsome guy!" he preened, gnashing his fine set of teeth together with glee.

Snappy was terribly proud of his sharp fangs, and fine good looks. He strutted up and down the river bank for all to see.

"I'm a star!" he said. "My face will be known throughout the world!"

"Thanks for letting us take your picture," said the expedition leader.

"No problem," said Snappy. "Any time!"

"And, as your reward, here's the truck load of chocolate you asked for," said the leader.

"How delicious!" said Snappy. "Most kind of you. Thank you so much."

When they had gone, Snappy lay sunning himself on the river bank, daydreaming of fame and fortune, and popping chocolate after chocolate into his big, open mouth.

Just then, along slithered Snake.

"What's thissss?" he hissed. "A crocodile eating chocolate? How very sssstrange!"

"Not at all!" snapped Snappy. "All crocodiles love chocolate. It's just that most of them aren't smart enough to know how to get hold of it."

"Well, if you're so sssmart, you ssshould know that too much chocolate will make your teeth fall out!" hissed Snake.

"What rot!" said Snappy, crossly. "For your information, I've got perfect teeth."

"Lucky you!" said Snake, and slithered off into the bushes.

So Snappy carried on munching happily, eating his way through the mound of chocolate. He had chocolate for breakfast, chocolate for lunch and chocolate for dinner.

"Ooh, yummy!" he grinned, licking his lips and smiling a big, chocolatey smile. "This is heaven."

"You won't be saying that when you are too fat to float in the river," said Parrot, who had been watching him from a tree.

"Nonsense!" scoffed Snappy. "I've got a very fine figure, I'll have you know!"

"If you say so," said Parrot, and flew off into the jungle.

Days and weeks passed, and Snappy happily carried on eating chocolate after chocolate, until at last it was all gone.

"Back to the river to catch my next meal, then," Snappy thought miserably. "Though I'd much rather have more chocolate!"

But, when Snappy slid into the river, instead of bobbing gently at the surface, he sank straight to the bottom, and his stomach rested in the mud.

"Oh dear, what's happened to the river?" Snappy wondered aloud to himself. "It's very hard to float in today,"

"Even for someone with such a fine figure as you?" jeered Parrot, watching from the trees. Snappy didn't answer. He just sank further beneath the water so that only his two beady eyes could be seen, and gave Parrot a very hard stare.

The next morning when he awoke there was a terrible pain in his mouth. It felt like someone was twisting and tugging on his teeth. "Oww, my teeth hurt!" he cried.

"Sssurely not!" hissed Snake, dangling down from a tree. "After all, you have sssuch perfect teeth!" and he slunk away again, snickering.

Snappy knew what he had to do. He set off down the river to visit Mr Drill the dentist.

It seemed such a long, hard walk, and by the time he got there he was puffing and panting.

"Open wide!" said Mr Drill, an anteater, peering down his long nose into Snappy's gaping mouth. "Oh dear. This doesn't look good at all. What have you been eating, Snappy? Now show me where it hurts."

"Here," said Snappy pointing miserably into his mouth, and feeling rather ashamed, "and here, and here, and here..."

"Well, there's nothing for it," said Mr Drill, "they'll have to come out!" And so out they came!

Before long, another photography expedition arrived in the jungle.

"Say cheese!" said the expedition leader.

"CHEESE!" smiled Snappy, stepping out from behind a tree. But, instead of a flash of cameras, Snappy met with howls of laughter, as the photographers fell about holding their sides.

"I thought you said Snappy was a handsome crocodile with perfect teeth!" they cried, looking at the leader. "He should be called Gappy, not Snappy!"

Poor Snappy slunk away into the bushes and cried. It was all his own fault for being so greedy and eating all that chocolate.

"There, there," said Mr Drill, patting his arm. "We'll soon fit you out with some fine new teeth."

And from then on, Snappy vowed he would never eat chocolate again!

Smelly Pup

All the animals were gathered in the barn. "It has come to our attention," said Mrs Hen to Smelly Pup, "that you are in need of a bath. You haven't had one all summer. Even the pigs are complaining!"

Smelly Pup just laughed. "Take a bath? That'll be the day!" he said, and off he went.

Outside Smelly Pup strolled through the farmyard, muttering, "What a crazy idea. I'm a dog. I do dog things… like chasing cats!" The farm cat leapt up hissing as Smelly Pup came racing towards her. He chased her all around the farmyard. Then, just as he was about to catch up, she sprang into the air. Smelly Pup took a great leap after her… and landed in the pond with a SPLASH!

"Silly Pup!" smirked the cat as she watched, perched on the branch of a nearby tree.

The ducks quacked as he spluttered and splashed, chasing them through the water! The water felt cool and refreshing on his fur. After a while, he came out and rolled on the nice muddy bank. "That was fun," he said. "Maybe I could get used to baths after all!"

Jello on the Plate

Jello on the plate,
  Jello on the plate,
Wibble, wobble,
  Wibble, wobble,
Jello on the plate.

Candies in the jar,
  Sweeties in the jar,
Shake them up,
  Shake them up,
Sweeties in the jar.

Candles on the cake,
  Candles on the cake,
Blow them out,
  Blow them out,
Puff, PUFF, PUFF!

Polly Put the Kettle On

Polly put the kettle on,
  Polly put the kettle on,
Polly put the kettle on,
We'll all have tea.

Sukey take it off again,
  Sukey take it off again,
Sukey take it off again,
  They've all gone away.

I Scream

I scream, you scream,
We all scream for ice-cream!

Little Jack Horner

Little Jack Horner,
  Sat in a corner,
Eating a Christmas pie.
  He put in his thumb,
And pulled out a plum,
  And said, "What a good boy am I!"

Ten Green Bottles

Ten green bottles, standing on a wall,
  Ten green bottles, standing on a wall,
And if one green bottle should accidentally fall,
  There'd be nine green bottles, standing on a wall.

Nine green bottles, standing on a wall,
  Nine green bottles, standing on a wall,
  And if one green bottle should accidentally fall,
    There'd be eight green bottles, standing on a wall.

Eight green bottles, standing on a wall,
  Eight green bottles, standing on a wall,
And if one green bottle should accidentally fall,
  There'd be seven green bottles, standing on a wall.

(continue with seven green bottles etc...)

Dibbity, Dibbity, Dibbity, Doe

Dibbity, dibbity, dibbity, doe,
  Give me a pancake
And I'll go.
  Dibbity, dibbity, dibbity, ditter,
Please to give me
  A bit of a fritter.

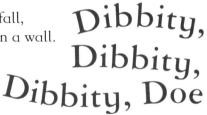

A Peanut

A peanut sat on the railroad track,
  His heart was all a-flutter;
Along came a train—the 9:15—
  Toot, toot, peanut butter!

Pat-a-Cake

Pat-a-cake, pat-a-cake, baker's man,
  Bake me a cake, as fast as you can.
Pat it and prick it and mark it with B,
  And put it in the oven for Baby and me.

Hazel Squirrel Learns a Lesson

Hazel Squirrel had the finest tail of all the animals that lived beside Looking-Glass Pond.

It was fluffier than Dilly Duck's tail… bushier than Harvey Rabbit's tail… and swooshier than everybody's!

Each morning Hazel groomed her tail and admired her reflection in the pond. "I really do have a beautiful tail!" she would say, smiling at herself in the silvery water.

Sometimes Hazel played with her friends, but it usually ended in tears.

"You splashed my lovely tail!" Hazel would shout crossly, when she played leap-frog with Webster. "You're getting my tail dirty, Harvey!" she would moan very grumpily, when they played digging.

Soon, Hazel stopped playing with her friends altogether.

"I'm far too busy brushing my tail!" she said when they came to call. "Come back some other time."

One morning as usual, Hazel was admiring her tail by the pond. Suddenly, she had a funny thought. She couldn't remember the last time she had seen her friends.

Hazel looked at her reflection in the pond. Staring back was a strange face… a cross face… a grumpy face. It was Hazel's face! Hazel couldn't believe her eyes. "No wonder my friends don't visit me any more," she cried. "I've forgotten how to smile!"

The next day Hazel called for her friends. They had such fun playing leap-frog and digging muddy holes that she forgot all about her tail. "From now on," she laughed, "the only time I'll look at my reflection is to practice smiling!"

Teddy Bear Tears

"**B**oo hoo! I want to go home!"
As a little fairy called Mavis
flew past the garbage dump, holding her nose, she heard an
unmistakable sound coming from the other side of a very smelly pile
of garbage.

"Oh dear. Those sound like teddy bear tears," she said to herself.
"I'd better go and see if I can help."

She flew down to take a look, and, sure enough, there amongst a heap
of old potato peelings and banana skins sat a very old, very sad teddy
indeed. Mavis sat and held his paw, while he told her tearfully what
had happened:

"My owner, Matilda, was told to clean out her room. She's terribly
messy, but she's sweet and kind," Teddy sniffed. "She threw me out with
an old blanket by mistake—she didn't realise I was tucked up having a
sleep inside it. Then some men in a big, dirty truck came and emptied
me out of the garbage can and brought me here. But I want to go
home!" And with that poor Teddy started to cry again.

"There, there," said Mavis. "I'll help to get you home. But first I'll
need two teddy bear tears." She unscrewed the lid of a little jar, and
scooped two big salty tears into it from Teddy's cheeks.

"What do you need those for?" asked Teddy, feeling rather bewildered.

"Just a little fairy magic!" said Mavis. "Now wait here, and I promise I'll be back soon." And with a wave of her wand, she disappeared.

Teddy pulled the blanket around him, and sat trying to be brave, and not to cry. He stayed like that all night, feeling cold and alone and frightened. How he wished he was back in his warm, cozy home.

Meanwhile Mavis was very busy. She flew back and forth around the neighborhood, until she heard the sound of sobbing coming from an open window. She flew down onto the windowsill and peered inside. A little girl was lying on the bed, with her mommy sitting beside her.

"I want my teddy!" she cried.

"Well if you weren't so messy, Matilda, you wouldn't lose things," said Mommy gently.

"But I cleaned my room today!" said Matilda.

"Well, try and go to sleep now," said Mommy, kissing her goodnight, "and we'll look for Teddy in the morning."

Mavis watched as poor Matilda lay sobbing into her pillow, until at last she fell fast asleep. Then Mavis flew down from the windowsill, took out the little jar, and rubbed Teddy's tears onto Matilda's sleeping eyes. With a little fizzle of stars, the fairy magic began to work, and Matilda started to dream. She could see an old tire, a newspaper, some tin cans, some orange peel, a blanket... wait a minute, it was her blanket, and there, wrapped inside it was her teddy, with a big tear running down his cheek! Teddy was at the garbage dump!

The next morning, Matilda woke with a start, and remembered her dream at once. She ran downstairs to the kitchen, where Mommy was making breakfast, and told her all about it.

"We have to go to the garbage dump! We have to save Teddy!" said Matilda.

Mommy tried to explain that it was just a dream, but Matilda wouldn't listen, she was sure she was right. So in the end they set off to take a look.

They arrived just as a big machine was scooping up the trash and heading for the

crusher. And there, on top of the scoop, clinging to the edge, was Teddy!

Mavis appeared, hovering in the air above him.

"Don't worry, we'll save you!" she said. She waved her wand in a bright flash above Teddy. Matilda looked up and spotted him at once.

"There he is!" she cried, pointing frantically at Teddy. "He's going to be squashed! Mommy, do something, quick!" Mommy ran up to the man driving the machine, waving her arms in the air.

He stopped his machine just in time.

Soon Teddy and Matilda were reunited, and there were more tears, although this time they were happy ones. And from then on, Matilda's room was the tidiest room you have ever seen.

Terrible Tongue Twisters

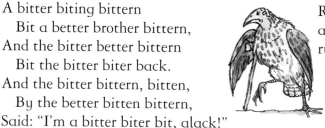

A bitter biting bittern
  Bit a better brother bittern,
And the bitter better bittern
  Bit the bitter biter back.
And the bitter bittern, bitten,
  By the better bitten bittern,
Said: "I'm a bitter biter bit, alack!"

Ruby Rugby's brother bought
and brought her back some
rubber baby-buggy bumpers.

Three free throws.

Silly Sally swiftly shooed seven silly sheep.
  The seven silly sheep Silly Sally shooed
shilly-shallied south.
  These sheep shouldn't sleep in a shack;
sheep should sleep in a shed.

Lily ladles little
Letty's lentil soup.

Six short slow shepherds.

I saw Esau kissing Kate. I saw Esau,
he saw me, and she saw I saw Esau.

The sixth sick sheik's
sixth sheep's sick.

A flea and a fly flew up in a flue.
Said the flea, "Let us fly!"
Said the fly, "Let us flee!"
So they flew through a flaw in the flue.

How much wood would a woodchuck chuck
  if a woodchuck could chuck wood?
He would chuck, he would, as much as he could,
  and chuck as much wood as a woodchuck would
if a woodchuck could chuck wood.

Betty and Bob brought
back blue balloons
from the big bazaar.

Red lorry,
yellow lorry,
red lorry,
yellow lorry.

Of all the felt I ever felt,
    I never felt a piece of felt
Which felt as fine as that felt felt,
    When first I felt that felt hat's felt.

I need not your needles, they're needless to me;
    For kneading of noodles, 'twere needless, you see;
But did my neat knickers but need to be kneed,
    I then should have need of your needles indeed.

Three gray geese in a green field grazing,
    Gray were the geese and green was the grazing.

A skunk sat on a stump and
thunk the stump stunk, but the
stump thunk the skunk stunk.

Timothy Titus took two ties
To tie two tups to two tall trees,
To terrify the terrible Thomas a Tullamees.
How many T's in *that*?

Betty Botter bought some butter,
    "But," she said, "this butter's bitter.
If I put it in my batter,
    It will make my batter bitter.
But a bit of better butter,
    That would make my batter better."
So she bought a bit of butter,
    Better than her bitter butter,
And she put it in her batter,
    And the batter was not bitter.
So 'twas better Betty Botter
    Bought a bit of better butter.

Six thick thistle sticks.
Six thick thistles stick.

Moses supposes his toeses are roses,
    But Moses supposes erroneously;
For nobody's toeses are posies of roses
    As Moses supposes his toeses to be.

Mermaid Marina

In a magical cave, down at the bottom of the deep blue sea, lives Marina, a beautiful mermaid with a shimmering tail. She glides through the water, searching for shiny pearls and sparkling shells.

Coral the dolphin is Marina's very best friend. They love to twirl and dive through the crystal blue waters, and play hide-and-seek amongst the colorful seaweed.

Today there is great excitement at the bottom of the sea. It's the Sea King's birthday and there will be a party.

Marina is getting ready. She puts on a pretty necklace made from glistening pearls, a bracelet and some tiny starfish earrings.

"How do I look, Coral?" she asks her friend. Coral flaps her fins and does a special dolphin twirl—Marina looks wonderful! Finally, the mermaid brushes her beautiful long hair and weaves some tiny blue sea-flowers into it. Then, with a flick of their tails, Marina and Coral head off for the party.

When they arrive at the palace, the other mermaids are amazed—Marina looks so pretty!

"Happy Birthday, Your Majesty!" she says, and gives the king her present—a precious pearl.

"Thank you, Marina," says the king, "it's almost as lovely as you are."

Granny Casts a Spell

Susie was very fond of her Granny. Each day, when Susie got home from school, Granny was always there, sitting by the fire, knitting. Granny knitted so fast that sometimes it seemed as though the knitting needles sparked in the firelight.

"Do you know," Granny would say, "that I'm really a witch?" Susie always laughed when Granny said that because she didn't look at all like a witch. She had a smiling face and kind eyes and she never wore black. Not ever. When Granny wasn't looking, Susie would take a peek inside her wardrobe just in case she might find a broomstick or a witch's hat. But she never found so much as a book of spells.

"I don't believe you're a witch," said Susie.

"I am," replied Granny, "and I'll cast a spell one day. You'll know when that day comes, for my needles will start to knit by themselves."

After that, Susie kept a careful watch over Granny's needles, but they always lay quite still in the basket of knitting.

One day, Susie was playing in her yard when she heard the sound of weeping. The sound seemed to be coming from under the old tree in the corner.

124

She walked towards the tree and as she did so the crying noise got louder, but she could not see anyone there. Then she looked down at her feet and there —sitting on a mossy stone—was a tiny little man. He was neatly dressed in a yellow velvet vest and knickers. On his feet were beautiful, shiny, buckled shoes, and a three-cornered hat with a wren's feather in it trembled on his shaking head. When the little man saw Susie, he stopped crying and started to dab his eyes with a fine lace handkerchief.

"Whatever can the matter be?" asked Susie, crouching down.

"Oh dear, oh dear!" sobbed the little man. "I am the fairy princess's tailor and she has asked me to make her a lovely gown to wear to the May Ball tonight, but a wicked elf has played a trick on me and turned all my fine gossamer fabric into bats' wings. Now I shall never be able to make the princess's gown and she will be very angry with me." He started to cry again.

"Don't cry!" said Susie. "I'm sure I can help. My Granny's got a sewing basket full of odds and ends. I'll see if she's got anything nice for a party dress. I'm sure she won't mind sparing some—after all, you won't need much," she said. At that, the little man looked a bit more cheerful.

"Wait here," said Susie, "while I run indoors and see." She ran up the yard path and in through the back door.

"Granny, Granny!" she called. She ran into the living room expecting to find Granny knitting by the fire. But Granny had her eyes closed and she was whispering to herself. On her lap was her knitting—and the needles were moving all by themselves, so that the yarn danced up and down on the old lady's knees.

At first Susie was too astounded to move. Then she thought, "I hope Granny's not casting a bad spell. I must see if the little tailor is alright."

She ran back down the garden path and there sat the tailor, surrounded by a great pile of gorgeous gossamer, shining in the sunlight.

"I've never seen such fine material—ever!" he exclaimed. "But where did it come from? I just closed my eyes to dab them with my hanky and when I opened them again—there it was!"

"I don't know," said Susie, "but I think my Granny might have had something to do with it."

"Well, I'd never be able to thank her enough," said the tailor. "I shall be able to make the finest gown in the whole of fairyland. The princess will dance all night in the prettiest dress there ever was. I'm also indebted to you, for it was you who helped me in the first place. I would like it very much if you came to the May Ball, too."

"Why, thank you so much," Susie replied, "I should like that very much." She didn't want to hurt the tailor's feelings but she knew she couldn't go—she was far too big to go to a fairy ball!

"Well, I must get on with the dress now," said the little man, reaching for a pair of fairy scissors. "See you tonight!" And with that he vanished.

That night, Susie wondered if the fairies really were having a ball. How she longed to be there! Once she thought she heard a tapping at the window. Was that the fairy tailor she saw through the glass— or was she imagining it? In the middle of the night she awoke with a start. There was a click, clicking noise at the end of her bed.

"Granny is that you?" asked Susie.

"Yes, dear," replied Granny. "I couldn't sleep, so I decided to do some knitting. All at once the needles started twitching, so I knew it was time to cast a spell. What is your wish, Susie?"

"I... I..." stammered Susie, "I want to go to the May Ball," she blurted.

"Then you shall, my dear," said Granny.

In an instant, Susie felt herself shrinking and when she looked down she saw she was wearing a beautiful gown and tiny satin slippers. Then she floated on gossamer wings out through the window and off to the Ball.

The next morning, Susie woke up in her bed. Had it all been a dream—the revelry, the fairy food, the frog band, the dance with the fairy prince? Then she saw something peeping out from under her pillow. And what do you think it was? It was a tiny, tiny shred of the finest gossamer fabric.

Little Jack Jingle

Little Jack Jingle,
   He used to live single:
But when he got tired of this kind of life,
   He left off being single, and lived with his wife.

Harry Parry

O rare Harry Parry,
   When will you marry?
When apples and pears are ripe.
   I'll come to your wedding,
Without any bidding,
   And dance and sing all the night.

Young Roger Came Tapping

Young Roger came tapping at Dolly's window,
   Thumpaty, thumpaty, thump!
He asked for admittance, she answered him "No!"
   Frumpaty, frumpaty, frump!
"No, no, Roger, no! as you came you may go!"
   Stumpaty, stumpaty, stump!

Jack, Jack, the Bread's a-Burning

Jack, Jack, the bread's a-burning,
   All to a cinder;
If you don't come and fetch it out
   We'll throw it through the window.

Robin and Richard

Robin and Richard were two pretty men;
 They laid in bed till the clock struck ten;
Then up starts Robin and looks at the sky,
 Oh! brother Richard, the sun's very high:

The bull's in the barn threshing the corn,
 The cock's on the dunghill blowing his horn,
The cat's at the fire frying of fish,
 The dog's in the pantry breaking his dish.

Little Tommy Tittlemouse

Little Tommy Tittlemouse
 Lived in a little house;
He caught fishes
 In other men's ditches.

Tom, Tom, the Piper's Son

Tom, Tom, the piper's son,
 Stole a pig, and away he run.
The pig was eat, and Tom was beat,
 And Tom went roaring down the street.

Jack and Guy

Jack and Guy went out in the rye,
 And they found a little boy with one black eye.
Come, says Jack, let's knock him on the head.
 No, says Guy, let's buy him some bread;
You buy one loaf and I'll buy two,
 And we'll bring him up as other folk do.

A Hat Like That

Heather the cow took great care of her appearance. She had the shiniest hooves and the glossiest coat. She had already won three rosettes at the Country Show, and she wanted to win more.

One windy afternoon, when Heather was standing near a hedge, she found a beautiful straw hat on a branch. It had a couple of holes in it, but an elegant cow has to put her ears somewhere!

She strolled back across the field with her nose in the air, and the hat placed firmly on her head. Heather couldn't wait to show it off to her friends.

But Poppy, Annabel and Emily simply carried on munching. Heather tried a tiny ladylike cough. The munching didn't stop for a second. So Heather coughed a little louder. The munching grew louder.

Heather couldn't bear it any longer. "Haven't you noticed it?" she mooed.

"Did I hear something?" asked Emily.

"It was me!" cried Heather, stamping her hoof crossly.

"Oh, so it was," said Annabel, and returned to a particularly juicy clump of green grass.

"Oh dear! I'm feeling rather sleepy, I think I'll just have a little snooze," said Poppy.

"And I'm going for a walk," said Emily.

Heather was not a patient cow. "Look at my hat!" she cried.

Of course, the other cows had noticed the hat, but they loved to tease their friend.

"I always think," said Poppy, "that hats are rather... old-fashioned."

"Nonsense," Heather replied. "Only the most fashionable cows are wearing them."

"It's new then, is it?" asked Annabel.

"Certainly!" Heather replied. "It's the very latest style."

"Didn't Mrs MacDonald have a hat like that a few years ago?" asked Emily.

"I don't think so!" Heather said firmly. "Mrs MacDonald is lovely, but she's not what you would call stylish. Only a prize-winning cow could carry off a hat like this."

"If you say so, dear," mooed Annabel.

That evening, the cows ambled into the farmyard to be milked. Before long, all the other animals had gathered round.

"They're admiring my hat!" whispered Heather to Poppy.

But the giggling and chuckling didn't sound as if they thought Heather looked beautiful. It sounded more like animals who thought she looked rather silly.

"Well, well! So that's what happened to Scarecrow Sam's hat!" cried Old MacDonald.

Nowadays, if Heather starts putting on airs and graces, Poppy, Emily and Annabel know just what to do—they start talking about hats, and Heather tiptoes away.

Elephant

H ere is Baby Elephant.
Baby Elephant plays with his friends, and he helps them, too.

"Giraffe, you've lost your patterns in the mud," said Baby Elephant. "I'll spray you with my trunk."

"Lion, you look too hot," said Baby Elephant. "I'll shade you with my big ears."

"Monkey, you look very tired," said Baby Elephant. "I'll carry you on my back."

"Oh no. Rhino! You've fallen in the river," said Baby Elephant. "Hold on to my tail very tightly, and I will pull you out."

After his hard work helping his friends, Baby Elephant decided to have a rest under a tree.

"We'll all stay close to Baby Elephant," said his friends, "to make sure he is safe while he rests."

Tiger

Baby Tiger lived in the jungle. One day he fell fast asleep, and his friends could not find him.

"Where is Baby Tiger?" they asked.

Monkey climbed to the top of the highest tree. Rhino ran fast along the riverbank. Elephant searched deep in the jungle.

"Where are you, Baby Tiger?" they called, as loudly as they could.

Then Elephant gave such a loud trumpet that Baby Tiger was woken up.

"Here I am," called Baby Tiger, and with a sleepy yawn and a stretch he waved a stripy paw.

"Baby Tiger! We've been looking everywhere for you," said the animals.

"We couldn't see you because of your stripes," said Monkey.

"We missed you, Baby Tiger," they said, giving him a great big hug.

Jack and the Beanstalk

Jack was a lively young boy who lived with his mother in a tiny little cottage in the country.

Jack and his mother were very poor. They had straw on the floor, and many panes of glass in their windows were broken. The only thing of value that was left was a cow.

One day, Jack's mother called him in from the yard, where he was chopping logs for their stove. "You will have to take Daisy the cow to market and sell her," she said sadly.

As Jack trudged along the road to market, he met a strange old man.

"Where are you taking that fine milking cow?" asked the man.

"To market, sir," replied Jack, "to sell her."

"If you sell her to me," said the man, "I will give you these beans. They are special, magic beans. I promise you won't regret it."

When Jack heard the word "magic", he became

very excited. He quickly swapped the cow for the beans, and ran all the way home.

Jack rushed through the cottage door. "Mother! Mother!" he called. "Where are you?"

"Why are you home so soon?" asked Jack's mother, coming down the stairs. "How much did you get for the cow?"

"I got these," said Jack, holding out his hand. "They're magic beans!"

"What?" shrieked his mother. "You sold our only cow for a handful of beans? You silly boy, come here!"

Angrily, she snatched the beans from Jack's hand and flung them out of the window and into the yard. Jack was sent to bed with no supper that night.

The next morning, Jack's rumbling stomach woke him early. His room was strangely dark. As he got dressed, he glanced out of his window—and what he saw took his breath away.

Overnight, a beanstalk had sprung up in the yard. Its trunk was almost as thick as Jack's cottage and its top was so tall that it disappeared into the clouds.

Jack yelled with excitement and rushed outside. As he began to climb the beanstalk, his mother stood at the bottom and begged for him to come back down, but he took no notice.

At last, tired and very hungry, Jack reached the top. He found himself in a strange land full of clouds. He could see something glinting in the

distance and
began walking
towards it.

Eventually he
reached the
biggest castle he
had ever seen.
Maybe he could
find some food in
the kitchen there?

He crept carefully under the front door and ran straight into an
enormous foot!

"What was that?" boomed a female voice, and the whole room shook.
Jack found himself looking into a huge eye. Suddenly, he was whisked
into the air by a giant hand!

"Who are you?" roared the voice.

"I'm Jack," said Jack, "and I'm tired and hungry. Please can you give
me something to eat and a place to rest for a while?"

The giant woman was a kind old lady and took pity on the tiny boy.
"Don't make a sound," she whispered. "My husband doesn't like boys
and will eat you if he
finds you." Then she
gave Jack a crumb of
warm bread and
a thimble full of
hot soup.

He was just eating
the last drop when
the woman said,

"Quick! Hide in the closet! My husband's coming!"

From inside the dark closet, Jack could hear the approach of thundering footsteps. Then a deep voice bellowed, *"Fee, fie, foe, fum, I smell the blood of an Englishman! Be he alive or be he dead, I'll grind his bones to make my bread!"*

Jack peeped out through a knothole in the closet door, and saw a huge giant standing beside the table.

"Wife!" shouted the giant. "I can smell a boy in the house!"

"Nonsense, dear," said the giant's wife soothingly. "All you can smell is this lovely dinner I have made for you. Now sit down and eat."

When the giant had gobbled up his dinner and a huge bowl of dessert, he shouted, "Wife! Bring me my gold! I wish to count it!"

Jack saw the giant's wife bring out several enormous sacks of coins. The giant picked one up and a cascade of gold fell onto the table top.

Then Jack watched the giant count the coins, one by one. The giant began to stack them up in piles as he worked.

After a while, he started to yawn, and, not long after, Jack saw that he had fallen asleep. Soon Jack heard very loud snoring!

"It's time I made a move!" Jack said to himself. And, quick as a flash, he leapt out of the closet, grabbed a sack of gold, slid down the table leg and ran for the door.

But the giant's wife heard him. "Stop, thief!" she screamed at the top of her voice, which woke her husband. He jumped up in a hurry and ran after Jack, shouting loudly, "Come back!"

Jack ran until he came to the top of the beanstalk. Then, with the giant still after him, he scrambled down as fast as he could.

"Mother!" he called, as he got closer to the ground. "Mother, get the ax, quickly!"

By the time Jack reached the bottom, his mother was there with the ax. She chopped down the beanstalk, and the giant came crashing down with it—he never got up again!

Now that they had the gold, Jack and his mother were very rich. They wouldn't have to worry about anything ever again and they lived happily ever after.

The Apple Tree

Here is the tree with leaves so green.
  Here are the apples that hang between.
When the wind blows the apples fall.
  Here is a basket to gather them all.

The Cherry Tree

Once I found a cherry stone,
  I put it in the ground,
And when I came to look at it,
  A tiny shoot I found.

The shoot grew up and up each day,
  And soon became a tree.
I picked the rosy cherries then,
  And ate them for my tea.

Here We Go Round the Mulberry Bush

Here we go round the mulberry bush,
  The mulberry bush, the mulberry bush,
Here we go round the mulberry bush,
  On a cold and frosty morning.

This is the way we wash our hands,
  Wash our hands, wash our hands,
This is the way we wash our hands,
  On a cold and frosty morning.

Here we go round the mulberry bush,
  The mulberry bush, the mulberry bush,
Here we go round the mulberry bush,
  On a cold and frosty morning.

This is the way we wash our clothes,
  Wash our clothes, wash our clothes,
This is the way we wash our clothes,
  On a cold and frosty morning.

Here we go round the mulberry bush,
  The mulberry bush, the mulberry bush,
Here we go round the mulberry bush,
  On a cold and frosty morning.

Lavender's Blue

Lavender's blue, dilly, dilly, lavender's green,
 When I am king, dilly, dilly, you shall be queen;
Call up your men, dilly, dilly, set them to work,
 Some to the plow, dilly, dilly, some to the cart;
Some to make hay, dilly, dilly, some to thresh corn;
 Whilst you and I, dilly, dilly, keep ourselves warm.

Dancing Round the Maypole

Dancing round the maypole,
 Dancing all the day,
Dancing round the maypole,
 On the first of May,
Dancing round the maypole,
 What a merry bunch,
Dancing round the maypole,
 Till it's time for lunch.

Dancing round the maypole,
 Shouting out with glee,
Dancing round the maypole,
 Till it's time for tea.
Dancing round the maypole,
 Blue and white and red,
Dancing round the maypole,
 Till it's time for bed.

I Had a Little Nut Tree

I had a little nut tree, nothing would it bear,
 But a silver nutmeg, and a golden pear;
The King of Spain's daughter came to visit me,
 And all for the sake of my little nut tree.
 I skipped over water, I danced over sea,
 And all the birds of the air
 couldn't catch me.

The Littlest Pig

Little Pig had a secret. He snuggled down in the warm hay with his brothers and sisters, looked up at the dark sky twinkling with stars, and smiled a secret smile to himself. Maybe it wasn't so bad being the littlest pig after all…

Not so long ago, Little Pig had been feeling quite fed up. He was the youngest and the smallest pig in the family. He had five brothers and five sisters who were all much bigger and fatter than him. The farmer's wife called him Runt, because he was the smallest pig of the litter.

His brothers and sisters teased him terribly. "Poor little Runtie," they said to him, giggling. "You must be the smallest pig in the world!"

"Leave me alone!" said Little Pig, and he crept off to the corner of the pigpen, where he curled into a ball, and started to cry. "If you weren't all so greedy, and let me have some food, maybe I'd be bigger!" he mumbled, sadly.

Every feeding time was the same—the others all pushed and shoved, until all that was left were the scraps. He would never grow bigger at this rate.

Then one day Little Pig made an important discovery. He was hiding in the corner of the pen, as usual, when he spied a little hole in the fence tucked away behind the feeding trough.

"I could fit through there!" thought Little Pig.

He waited all day until it was time for bed, and then, when he was sure that all of his brothers and sisters were fast asleep, he wriggled through the hole. Suddenly he was outside, free to go wherever he pleased. And what an adventure he had!

First, he ran to the henhouse and gobbled up the bowls of grain. Then he ran to the field and crunched up Donkey's carrots.

He ran to the vegetable patch and munched a row of cabbages. What a feast! Then, when he was full to bursting, he headed for home. On the way he stopped by the hedgerow. What was that lovely smell? He rooted around and found where it was coming from—a bank of wild strawberries.

Little Pig had never tasted anything quite so delicious.

"Tomorrow night, I'll start with these!"

THE LITTLEST PIG

he promised himself
as he trotted back
home to the
pigpen. He
wriggled back
through the
hole, and fell
fast asleep
snuggled up to his
mother, smiling very
contentedly.

Every night Little Pig continued his tasty adventures. He didn't mind when they pushed him out of the way at feeding time, he knew that a much better feast awaited him outside. Sometimes he would find the dog's bowl filled with scraps from the farmer's supper, or buckets of oats ready for the horses. "Yum, yum—piggy porridge!" he would giggle, and gobbled it up.

But, as the days and weeks went by, and Little Pig grew bigger and fatter, every night it became more of a squeeze to wriggle and push his way through the hole.

Little Pig knew that soon he would no longer be able to fit through the hole, but by then he would be big enough to stand up to his brothers and sisters. And for now he was enjoying his secret!

Loves to Sing!

Old MacDonald loves to sing,
  Whilst doing all his chores.
His wife just thanks her lucky stars,
  He does it when outdoors!

It's rather like a lost lamb's bleat,
  A hungry horse's neigh.
The kind of snort a piglet makes,
  When rolling in the hay!

So Old MacDonald's wife just cooks,
  Her husband gets no thinner,
Because MacDonald cannot sing,
  With his mouth full of dinner!

Did You Know?

Did you know ducks like to dance?
  Their pirouettes are grand.
And what is more,
  They can perform
On water or on land.

Did you know ducks like to dance?
  They shimmy and they shake.
And what is more,
  They can perform
A very fine Swan Lake!

Busy Farmer

When a very busy farmer,
  Goes upstairs to bed at night,
He simply can't stop wondering,
  If everything's all right.

Are the cows asleep and dreaming
  Are they trotting down the lane
Is the cockerel in the kitchen,
  Pecking at the pies again?

So a very busy farmer,
  Always rises at first light.
He simply cannot wait to check
  That everything's all right.

Where are You?

Doris Duck, Doris Duck,
  Where are you?
Here I am! Here I am!
  Dabbling in the dew.
Dora Duck, Dora Duck,
  Where are you?
Here I am, diving down,
  Which I love to do!
Ducklings all, ducklings all,
  Where are you?
Here we are, swimming round,
  Coming to splash YOU!

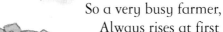

Watch Out!

When Percy the pig feels peckish,
　　There's very little doubt,
That he will gobble anything,
　　Animals, watch out!
He nibbles straw
　　At the stable door.
He chomps on weed
　　Where the ducklings feed.
He munches hay
　　When the cows are away.
He snacks on corn
　　If a sack is torn.
When Percy the pig feels peckish,
　　There's very little doubt,
That even Old MacDonald
　　Shouldn't leave his lunch about!

Kittens are Cuddly

Kittens are cuddly,
　　Kittens are sweet,
They dash round the farmyard,
　　On soft, furry feet.

And before very long,
　　They are kittens no more,
But cats who do nothing,
　　But stretch out and snore!

Back to the Farm

Old MacDonald went to town,
　　Three pigs under his arm.
One didn't want to go there,
　　So he ran back to the farm.

Old MacDonald went to town,
　　Two pigs under his arm.
One kicked the farmer on his knee,
　　And ran back to the farm.

Old MacDonald went to town,
　　One pig under his arm.
He bit the farmer on the nose,
　　Then ran back to the farm.

The piglets didn't want to go,
　　They said, "We like it here!"
MacDonald said, "Oh, all right then!"
　　And the pigs began to cheer!

Without a Growl

When Old MacDonald's work is done,
　　And twilight falls with the setting sun,
He sits down in his chair.
　　For he knows that he has a friend,
From day's beginning to day's end,
　　Bruce the farm dog
　　is there.

One Dark Night

Paws tiptoed out into the dark farmyard. Mommy had told him to stay in the barn until he was old enough to go out at night. But he was impatient. He had not gone far when something brushed past his ears. He froze as the fur on his neck began to rise. To his relief it was only a bat—there were plenty of those in the barn.

A loud hoot echoed through the trees— "Toowhit, Toowhoo!" and a great dark shape swooped down and snatched something up. "Just an owl," Paws told himself. "Some of those in the barn too. Nothing to be afraid of!" Creeping nervously on into the darkness, he wondered if this was such a good idea after all. Strange rustlings came from every corner, and he jumped as the old pig gave a loud grunt from the pigsty close by.

Then, all of a sudden, Paws froze in his tracks. Beneath the henhouse two eyes glinted in the darkness, as they came creeping towards him. This must be the fox Mommy had warned him of! But to his amazement he saw it was Mommy!

"Back to the barn!" she said sternly and Paws happily did as he was told. Maybe he would wait until he was older to go out at night, after all!

The Bear Will Have to Go

While Lucy slept in the shade of a tree, Cuthbert went for a walk into the woods and was soon quite lost. He had no idea which way was back, so he sat down and thought about what to do next.

When Lucy awoke, she looked around in surprise. Her teddy bear, Cuthbert, was missing. She thought someone had taken him, for she didn't know that when people are asleep their teddy bears come to life and like to go exploring.

"Cuthbert!" she called. "Cuthbert, where are you?"

He wasn't very far away. Lucy soon found him sniffing at a clump of moss.

"There you are!" she sighed. "I thought I'd lost you. What have you done with your vest?"

In fact, Lucy really had lost Cuthbert, for the bear she was now taking home was not a teddy bear at all, but a real baby bear cub! As they ran back through the woods, the bear in Lucy's arms kept very still. He stared straight ahead without blinking, and tried not to sneeze. Soon they were back home in Lucy's bedroom.

Lucy flung the bear on her bed, then went to run a bath.

"Time to escape!" thought the bear. He slid off the bed, pulling the covers after him. He ran over to the window and tried to climb up the curtains. They tore down and tumbled to a heap on the floor. Just then Lucy's mother came into the room. The bear froze. Then Lucy appeared.

"Look at this mess," said Lucy's mother. "You've been playing with that bear again. Please tidy up."

Lucy had no idea how her room had got in such a mess, but she quickly tidied up, took the bear into the bathroom and put him on the edge of the tub.

"Don't fall in," she said, and went to fetch a towel. The bear jumped into the tub with a great splash. He waved his paws wildly, sending sprays of soapy water across the room. When he heard footsteps, he froze and floated on his back in the water as if nothing was wrong. It was Lucy, followed by her mother. "Oh, Lucy! What a mess!"

"Cuthbert must have fallen in," cried Lucy, rubbing his wet fur with a towel.

"A teddy bear couldn't make all this mess on its own," said Lucy's mother. "Please clean it up."

Lucy looked carefully at Cuthbert. Something was different about him, but she just couldn't work out what it was.

That night, while Lucy slept, the bear tiptoed downstairs. He needed to get back to the woods where he belonged, but he was hungry. In the kitchen he found lots of food, and he had a feast.

When Lucy came down for a glass of milk she found him with food all over his paws. The bear froze. Then her mother appeared in the doorway, looking really angry.

"This is the last straw, Lucy," said her mother, crossly. "You have been very naughty today, and every time something happens you've got that bear with you. If there is any more bad behaviour like this, then the bear will have to go."

When her mother had gone back upstairs, Lucy looked carefully at the little furry bear.

"You're not Cuthbert are you?" she said. The bear looked back at her and blinked. Lucy gasped. "You're a real bear!"

Now all the mess made sense! Lucy could hardly believe she had made such a mistake. She stroked the bear gently and he licked her finger.

"I'd better get you back

to the woods before there's any more trouble," she said. "And I'd better try to find the real Cuthbert."

So early next morning, before her parents were awake, she crept out of the house carrying the bear. Out in the woods she put the bear on the ground. He licked her hand and padded away.

Lucy was sad to see the little bear go. She wiped a tear from her eye as she turned away... and there at the foot of a tree sat her teddy bear, Cuthbert! Lucy picked him up and hugged him.

"Where have you been?" she asked. "You'll never guess the trouble I've been in. What have you been doing all night?"

Cuthbert said nothing. He just smiled. What had he been doing all night? Well, that's another story!

Monday's Child is Fair of Face

Monday's child is fair of face,
   Tuesday's child is full of grace,
Wednesday's child is full of woe,
   Thursday's child has far to go,
Friday's child is loving and giving,
   Saturday's child works hard for his living,
And the child that is born on the Sabbath day
Is bonny and blithe, and good and gay.

Little Jumping Joan

Here am I, little jumping Joan.
   When nobody's with me,
  I'm always alone.

There Was a Little Girl

There was a little girl, and she had a little curl
   Right in the middle of her forehead;
When she was good she was very, very good,
   But when she was bad she was horrid.

Anna Maria

Anna Maria she sat on the fire;
   The fire was too hot, she sat on the pot;
The pot was too round, she sat on the ground;
   The ground was too flat, she sat on the cat;
The cat ran away with Maria on her back.

A Pretty Little Girl in a Round-eared Cap

A pretty little girl in a round-eared cap
   I met in the streets the other day;
She gave me such a thump,
   That my heart it went bump;
I thought I should have fainted away!
   I thought I should have fainted away!

Goldy Locks, Goldy Locks

Goldy locks, goldy locks,
   Wilt thou be mine?
Thou shall not wash dishes,
   Nor yet feed the swine;

But sit on a cushion,
   And sew a fine seam,
And feed upon strawberries,
   Sugar and cream.

Mr Punchinello

Oh! mother, I shall be married
   To Mr Punchinello.
   To Mr Punch,
   To Mr Joe,
   To Mr Nell,
   To Mr Lo,
   Mr Punch, Mr Joe,
   Mr Nell, Mr Lo,
   To Mr Punchinello.

Gilly Silly Jarter

Gilly Silly Jarter,
   Who has lost a garter?
In a shower of rain,
   The miller found it,
The miller ground it,
   And the miller gave it
To Silly again.

You Can Do It, Dilly Duck!

It was the night before Dilly's first swimming lesson.

"I've got a funny feeling in my tummy," said Dilly, as Mamma Duck kissed her goodnight.

"Don't worry!" replied her mother. "Just close your eyes tightly and you'll soon fall asleep." Dilly shut her eyes and tried to go to sleep. But all she could think about was the lesson.

"What if I sink?" she worried. Dilly pictured Mamma Duck's smiling face. "If Mamma Duck can float, perhaps I can, too," she thought. Then she snuggled down to go to sleep.

Suddenly Dilly opened her eyes. "But I'll get all wet!" she quacked, shaking her feathers. Dilly thought about her friend Webster the frog. "Webster loves getting wet," she remembered. "He says it's fun!"

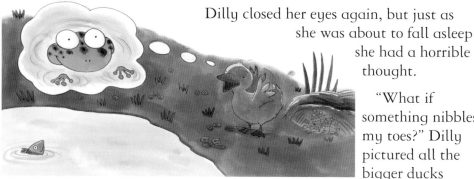

Dilly closed her eyes again, but just as she was about to fall asleep she had a horrible thought.

"What if something nibbles my toes?" Dilly pictured all the bigger ducks

doing duck-dives in the pond. "They're not afraid of what's under the water," she quacked, "so why should I be?" Dilly was wide awake early the next morning, and so were all her friends.

"You can do it, Dilly!" they cheered as she waddled slowly to the edge of the pond. She leaned forward and looked in, very timidly. There in the water was another little duckling gazing back at her. Dilly looked at the other little duckling. She was small and yellow with downy feathers, just like Dilly.

"Well, if you can do it, I guess I can too!"quacked Dilly bravely. SPLASH! She jumped right into the pond. "I can float!" cried Dilly, paddling along. "It's fun getting wet!" Then Dilly did a duck-dive.

"There's nothing scary under the water either!" she added, bobbing up again. "In fact, you are all right! I CAN do it!"

The Very Big Parcel

Once upon a time there lived an old man and his wife. They lived in a small house with a small, neat yard and they were very contented. What's more, they had very good friends and neighbors, with whom they shared everything. One day, there was a knock at the door and there stood the mailman with a huge parcel in his arms.

"My, oh my!" exclaimed the old man to his wife as he staggered into the kitchen with the enormous load.

"Whatever can it be?" wondered the old woman as the two of them stared at the parcel. "Perhaps it's a new set of china," she said.

"Or a new wheelbarrow," he said—and they began to think about all the great things there might be inside the parcel.

"Well, why don't we open it and see?" said the old lady at last—and so they did. They looked into the box and at first it seemed to be totally empty.

"Well, I never did!" cried the old man. And then he spotted something right in the corner of the box. He lifted it out into the light to examine it more carefully and discovered it was a single seed.

Well, the old man and his wife were most upset. Whereas before they were quite content, now that they had thought about all the things that might have been in the box they were bitterly disappointed by the seed. "Still," said the old man at last, "we'd better plant it anyway. Who knows, maybe we'll get a nice fresh lettuce from it."

So he planted the seed in the yard. Every day he watered the ground and soon a shoot appeared. The shoot grew into a strong young plant and then it grew taller and taller. Higher and higher it grew until it was a handsome tree. The man and his wife were excited to see fruits growing on the tree.

"I wonder if they're apples," the old man said. Each day he watered the tree and examined the fruits. One day he said to his wife, "The first fruit is ready to pick." He carefully reached up into the tree and picked the large red fruit. He carried it into the kitchen and put it on the table. Then he took a knife and cut the fruit in half. To his astonishment out poured a pile of gold coins. "Come quickly!" he called to his wife. Well, the pair of them danced around the kitchen for joy.

The old couple decided to spend just one gold coin and keep the rest. "After all," said the woman wisely, "we don't know what's in the other fruits. They may be full of worms." So they spent one gold coin in the town and put the rest aside.

The next day the old man picked another big red fruit and this, too, was full of gold.

After that the old couple were less careful with their money, thinking all the fruits must be full of gold. They had a wonderful time buying fine clothes and things for the house. Each day the man picked another fruit. Each day it was full of gold and each day they went into town and had a great time spending the money. But all the while the man forgot entirely to water the tree.

Meanwhile, the old couple's friends and neighbors started to gossip among themselves. They wondered where all the money was coming from and they began to resent the old couple. They noticed that they didn't buy anything for their friends, or even throw a party. Gradually their friends ignored them until the old couple were left with no friends at all. But they didn't even notice because they were so busy spending the gold coins.

Then one day the old man looked out into the yard and saw that the tree was all withered. He rushed outside and threw bucket after bucket of water over the tree, but all to no avail. He and his wife frantically picked the fruits left on the tree, but when they took them indoors they found to their dismay that they were cracked and gnarled. When they broke open the fruits they were full of dust.

"If only I had not been so thoughtless and remembered to water the tree!" cried the old man in anguish.

The next day the old couple looked out of the window to find that the tree had vanished. Now what were they to do? They had neglected their yard and now they had nothing to eat. They realised that they would have to sell their riches to buy food. Then they also needed new gardening tools, for theirs had grown rusty with neglect.

As the weeks passed, the old man and his wife gradually sold all the fine things they had bought, just to keep body and soul together. They felt truly miserable and sorry for the way they had treated their neighbors. They realised just how lonely they were without their friends.

"We have no money now," said the wife one day, "but let's have a party anyway—friendship is more valuable than any amount of gold coins."

So the old couple invited all their friends and neighbors round and they had a great party. The friends wondered what had happened to all the old couple's riches and what had happened to make the old couple so friendly once more, but I don't think they ever found out, do you?

Honey Bear and the Bees

One day, as Honey Bear woke from her dreams, her furry little nose started to twitch with excitement. She could smell her most favorite thing in the world—sweet, yummy honey! The smell was coming from a hollow tree stump nearby. She padded over and dipped in a large paw. How delicious the sweet, sticky honey tasted!

Honey Bear dipped her paw in again and again, digging deep into the tree stump to reach more of the lovely, sticky honey. This was the life! In fact, she dug so deep that, when she tried to take her great paw out, she found it was stuck fast! Just then, she heard a loud buzzing noise and looked up to see a huge swarm of angry bees returning to their hive!

Poor Honey Bear hollered as the bees flew around, stinging her all over! She tugged and tugged, and at last she pulled her paw free. The angry bees chased her all the way to the river where she sat cooling her burning skin. Just then, an irresistible smell reached her furry nose. It was coming from a hollow tree nearby.

"Mmm, honey!" said Honey Bear. "I'll just go and take a look… "

The Great Brown Owl

The brown owl sits in the ivy bush,
   And she looketh wondrous wise,
With a horny beak beneath her cowl,
   And a pair of large round eyes.

She sat all day on the selfsame spray,
   From sunrise till sunset;
And the dim, gray light it was all too bright
   For the owl to see in yet.

"Jenny Owlet, Jenny Owlet," said a merry little bird,
   "They say you're wondrous wise;
But I don't think you see, though you're looking at *me*
   With your large, round, shining eyes."

But night came soon, and the pale white moon
   Rolled high up in the skies;
And the great brown owl flew away in her cowl,
   With her large, round, shining eyes.

The Eagle

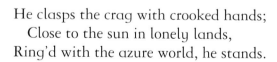

He clasps the crag with crooked hands;
   Close to the sun in lonely lands,
Ring'd with the azure world, he stands.

The wrinkled sea beneath him crawls;
   He watches from his mountain walls,
And like a thunderbolt he falls.

ALFRED, LORD TENNYSON

The Owl

When cats run home and light is come,
　And dew is cold upon the ground,
And the far-off stream is dumb,
　And the whirring sail goes round,
And the whirring sail goes round;
　Alone and warming his five wits,
The white owl in the belfry sits.

ALFRED, LORD TENNYSON

Little Trotty Wagtail

Little Trotty Wagtail, he went in the rain,
　And twittering, tottering sideways, he ne'er got straight again;
He stooped to get a worm, and looked up to get a fly,
　And then he flew away 'ere his feathers they were dry.

　　Little Trotty Wagtail, he waddled in the mud,
　　　And left his little foot-marks, trample where he would,
　　He waddled in the water-pudge, and waggle went his tail,
　　　And chirrupped up his wings to dry upon the garden rail.

Little Trotty Wagtail, you nimble all about,
　And in the dimpling water-pudge you waddle in and out;
Your home is nigh at hand and in the warm pig-stye;
　So, little Master Wagtail, I'll bid you a good-bye.

Monkey Mayhem

Mickey and Maxine Monkey had finished their breakfast of Mango Munch. Now they were rushing off to play.

"Be careful!" called their mom. "And please DON'T make too much noise!"

"We won't!" the two mischievous monkeys promised, leaping across to the next tree.

"Wheeee," screeched Mickey, and "Wa-hoooo!" hollered Maxine.

The noise echoed through the whole jungle—Mickey and Maxine just didn't know how to be quiet!

Ka-thunk! Mickey landed on a branch. Ka-clunk! Maxine landed beside him. Ker-aack!

"Ooohh noooo!" the monkeys hollered as the branch snapped.

"Yi-i-i-kes!" they shrieked, as they went tumbling down. Ker-thumpp! The jungle shook as the two monkeys crashed to the ground.

"Yipppeeee!" the monkeys cheered, jumping up happily.

"That was so much FUN!" exclaimed Maxine. "Let's go and get Chico Chimp and see if he wants to do it, too!" And the two monkeys scrambled back up to the tree tops, bellowing, "HEY, CHICO! COME AND PLAY WITH US!" as they swung through the branches.

All over the jungle, animals shook their heads and covered their ears. Couldn't anyone keep those naughty, noisy monkeys quiet?

Chico Chimp arrived to play with his friends. The three of them were having a great time swinging, tumbling and bouncing together when suddenly they stopped short. Grandpa Gorilla was standing in their path, glaring at them angrily.

"Go away, you mischief-makers," he said. "You've given us all enough headaches today. My grandson Gulliver is fast asleep by the river and, if you wake him up, I will be very, very upset!"

"Sorry," whispered Maxine, looking down at the ground. Everyone in the jungle knew it was a big mistake to upset Grandpa Gorilla!

"We'll be quiet," they promised.

Mickey, Maxine and Chico didn't know what to do until Mickey said, "Let's climb the coconut palm tree. We can do that quietly."

"Okay," the others agreed half-heartedly.

"I suppose it's better than doing nothing," said Maxine.

From their perch among the coconuts, the three friends could see right over the jungle.

They saw Jerome Giraffe showing his son Jeremy how to choose the juiciest, most tender leaves on a tree... and they saw Portia Parrot giving her daughter Penelope her first flying lesson. And right down below them, they saw little Gulliver Gorilla sleeping contentedly in the tall grass beside the river.

And—uh-oh! They saw something else, too... Claudia Crocodile was in the river. She was grinning and snapping her big, sharp teeth—and heading straight for Gulliver!

The friends didn't think twice. Maxine shouted, "GET UP, GULLIVER! GET UP RIGHT NOOOOOOWW!"

Then Mickey and Chico began throwing coconuts at Claudia.

SMAACCCK! they went, on Claudia's hard crocodile head.

"OWW-WOOW!" moaned Claudia.

"What's going on here?" Grandpa Gorilla shouted up into the coconut tree. "I thought I told you three to keep quiet!"

All the noise woke Gulliver. The little gorilla sat up, looked around, and ran to his grandpa, who was hurrying towards the river.

When Grandpa saw Claudia he realised what had happened. "I am so glad you're safe!" he said, giving Gulliver a great big gorilla hug. The three monkeys came down from the tree.

"We're sorry we made so much noise," Chico said.

By this time all the gorillas had gathered around, and so had most of the other animals.

"What's going on?" squawked Portia Parrot.

"Yes, what's all the commotion about?" asked Jerome Giraffe.

"These three youngsters are heroes," said Grandpa. "They have saved my grandson from being eaten by Claudia Crocodile!"

"I think you all deserve a reward," said Grandpa. "And I think it should be…"

"Hooray!" cheered all the other animals and then they held their breath in anticipation.

"…permission to be just as noisy as you like, whenever you like!" Grandpa Gorilla announced.

"YIPPEEE!" cheered Mickey, Maxine and Chico, in their loudest, screechiest voices. Their grins were almost as wide as the river.

"OH, NOOOOO!" all the other animals groaned together— but they were all smiling, too.

Bears Ahoy!

One summer's day, three little boys went for a picnic by the bank of a river. They took with them their swimming things, some cheese and pickle sandwiches and, of course, their teddy bears.

When they arrived, they found a small boat tied to a tree. The boys climbed on board, taking their teddies with them, and had a great game of pirates. The boys pretended to walk the plank, and soon they were all splashing about, playing and swimming in the river. They chased each other through the shallow water, and disappeared along the river and out of sight.

Bears Ahoy!

Now, the three bears left on board the boat did not get on very well together. Oscar was a small, honey-colored bear. He was good friends with Mabel, who had shaggy brown fur, but neither of them liked Toby. He was bigger than they were and he was a bully. He was always growling at the other bears and telling them what to do.

As soon as the boys were out of sight, Toby leapt to his feet. The boat rocked. Oscar and Mabel begged him to sit down.

"I'm a fearless sailor," cried Toby. "I've sailed the seven seas and now I'm going to sail them again."

Before the others realised what he was doing, Toby had untied the boat, and pushed it away from the bank. The boat lurched from side to side.

"Come on, crew. Look lively!" shouted Toby. "Do as I say or I'll make you walk the plank." Now that it was untied, the little blue boat began to drift out into the river. It turned sideways gently, then caught the main current and began to gather speed.

"Toby!" cried Oscar. "We're moving!"

"Of course we are, you big softie," growled Toby. "We're bold and fearless pirates on the high seas."

Oscar and Mabel clung together in fright, as the little boat sailed down the river, past fields and houses. "Help!" they shouted. "Toby, make it stop!" But Toby was having a great time.

"Ha, ha," shouted Toby. "This is the life!"

Oscar glanced over the side. He wished he hadn't. The sight of everything passing by so quickly made him feel seasick.

"Look out, Toby!" he cried. "We're going to hit the bank. Quickly, steer it away before we crash!"

But Toby did nothing. He simply sat and watched as the little boat careered along, gathering speed as it headed for the bank. Oscar and Mabel clutched the sides of the boat tightly, and clung on fast. They were feeling very frightened. The boat hit the bank with a thump and Toby fell forward. The boat swung round and headed for the middle of the river once more.

"Toby!" shouted Mabel. "Save us!"

But Toby was sitting in the bottom of the boat, rubbing a big bump on his head.

"I can't. I don't know how to sail a boat," he whimpered, feebly. He hid his face in his paws and began to cry. The boat zig-zagged on down the river, with the little bears clinging on to the sides in fright. In time, the river became wider and they could hear the cry of seagulls.

"Oh, Toby," cried Mabel. "We're heading for the sea. Do something!"

"Nobody likes me," wailed Toby. "Now we're going to sink to the bottom of the sea, and you won't like me either!"

Oscar wasn't listening. He had found a rope hanging from the sail. "Let's put the sail up and see if it will blow us to shore," he said.

"We'll be blown out to sea," wailed Toby, but Oscar ignored him, and carried on. The wind filled the sail and the little boat started moving forward. They sailed right across the bay to the far side, and blew up on to the beach.

"Oh, Oscar, you are a hero!" sighed Mabel, hugging him tight. "You saved us!"

Imagine the bears' surprise to see the three little boys running towards them along the beach—they had gone to find the coastguard and raise the alarm. There were hugs and kisses all round when they found the bears safe and sound. And you can be sure that, from that day on, Toby was a much wiser and kinder bear, and he never bullied the others again.

Fairy Fern

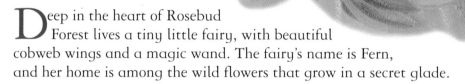

Deep in the heart of Rosebud
Forest lives a tiny little fairy, with beautiful
cobweb wings and a magic wand. The fairy's name is Fern,
and her home is among the wild flowers that grow in a secret glade.

Fern has a special friend—Sapphire the bluebird. They love to fly
through the forest, leaping over rays of sunlight, chasing pretty
butterflies. Then, by the light of the moon, Sapphire and Fern dance
and sing around a "fairy ring" with all their friends.

Today, Fairy Fern is really excited! There's to be a fairy parade.
Flora, the Fairy Queen, will choose the prettiest fairy dress.

FAIRY FERN

With a tap-tap of her wand, Fern magically changes into a dress of velvety rose petals and bluebells. Then, with a sprinkling of fairy dust, Fern makes a secret wish…

"Please let Queen Flora choose me!" she whispers.

But Fern has forgotten to get her friend ready! She weaves some flowers through Sapphire's feathers and adds a sprinkling of fairy dust.

Now for the final touch! Fairy Fern twists her hair up and pins it into place with a golden flower. Then, with a flutter of wings, they fly off to the parade.

Fairy Fern arrives just as Queen Flora is announcing the winner… "and the Golden Crown goes to… Fairy Fern!"

All the fairies cheer and flutter their wings. Fairy Fern smiles as the crown is placed on her head. She is the happiest fairy in the forest—her secret wish has come true.

Pop Goes the Weasel

Half a pound of tu'penny rice,
  Half a pound of treacle.
That's the way the money goes,
  POP! goes the weasel.

Hot Cross Buns!

Hot cross buns!
  Hot cross buns!
One a-penny, two a-penny,
  Hot cross buns!
If you have no daughters,
  Give them to your sons,
One a-penny, two a-penny,
  Hot cross buns!

Oats and Beans

Oats and beans and barley grow,
  Oats and beans and barley grow,
Do you or I or anyone know,
  How oats and beans and barley grow?

First the farmer sows his seeds,
  Then he stands and takes his ease,
Stamps his feet and claps his hands,
  Turns around to view the land.

Pease Pudding Hot

Pease pudding hot,
  Pease pudding cold,
Pease pudding in the pot,
  Nine days old.

Some like it hot,
  Some like it cold,
Some like it in the pot,
  Nine days old.

Sing a Song of Sixpence

Sing a song of sixpence,
    A pocket full of rye;
Four-and-twenty blackbirds
    Baked in a pie;
When the pie was opened,
    The birds began to sing;
Wasn't that a dainty dish,
    To set before a king?

Five Little Peas

Five little peas in a pea-pod pressed,
    One grew, two grew, and so did all the rest.
They grew, and they grew, and they did not stop,
    Until one day the pod went... POP!

Five Fat Sausages

Five fat sausages frying in a pan,
    All of a sudden one went "BANG!"
Four fat sausages, etc.
    Three fat sausages, etc.
Two fat sausages, etc.
    One fat sausage frying in a pan,
All of a sudden it went "BANG!"
    and there were NO sausages left!

Robin the Bobbin

Robin the Bobbin, the big-bellied Ben,
    He ate more meat than fourscore men;
He ate a cow, he ate a calf,
    He ate a butcher and a half;
He ate a church, he ate a steeple,
    He ate the priest and all the people!
        A cow and a calf,
            An ox and a half,
        A church and a steeple,
            And all the good people,
And yet he complained that his stomach wasn't full.

Chasing Tails

Barney had been chasing his tail all morning. Round and round he went, until he made himself feel quite dizzy.

"Can't you find something useful to do?" asked the cat, from where she sat watching him on the fence.

"What? Like chasing lazy cats?" said Barney, as he leapt towards her, barking fiercely.

Later, as he trotted around the farmyard, Barney thought about what the cat had said. He wished he could be more useful, but he was only a little pup. When he grew up, he would be a fine, useful farm dog, like his mom. Just then, he rounded the barn, and there in front of him waved a big, bushy tail…

"Here's a tail I can catch!" thought Barney playfully, and he sprang forward and sank his sharp little puppy teeth into it!

Now, the tail belonged to a sly fox, who was about to pounce on Mrs Hen and her chicks! The fox yelped in surprise, and ran away across the fields.

"Ooh, Barney, you saved us!" cried Mrs Hen.

The cat was watching from the fence. "Maybe all that practise chasing tails has come in useful after all!" she said.

Staying at Grandma's

Jack hugged his teddy bear tightly, while Mom packed his slippers and pajamas into a bag.

"Why can't I come with you?" he asked.

"Because Dad and I have to go away for one night," said Mom. "You're going to stay with Gran and Grandad. They can't wait to see you."

"But I'll be scared without you and Dad," whispered Jack.

"Don't worry," said Mom. "You'll have such a good time, you won't want to come home!"

Later that day, Gran and Grandad opened their front door, as Mom, Dad and Jack arrived in their car. Holly, Gran's little dog, peeped through her legs, wagging her tail with excitement. But soon, it was time for Jack to say goodbye to his mom and dad. Jack felt really sad. He didn't want them to leave. He hugged his mom tightly. "I'll miss you," he said.

Mom gave Jack a big hug. "We'll be back tomorrow morning, I promise," she smiled. Then, she and Dad got into the car.

As they drove away, Jack waved until he couldn't see the car anymore. His eyes filled with tears. "Come on, Jack," said Gran, giving him a big cuddle. "We're going to have such a good time. Guess where Grandad's taking us this afternoon?" Jack wiped his eyes and shook his head.

"Um... I don't know," he sniffed. Grandad gave him a tissue. Just then, Holly came bounding over. "Hello, Holly," said Jack, looking more cheerful. He rubbed her big, floppy ears. Jack loved Holly and, just for tonight, he could pretend she was his dog.

"Grandad," asked Jack, "where are we going this afternoon?"

"It's a surprise," said Grandad. "But we'll need the car. Why don't we give it a good clean?" So, Grandad gave Jack a big, yellow sponge and a bucket of soapy water. Soon, bubbles filled the air. They even went on Holly's nose!

Just then, Gran called to Jack from the kitchen. "I'm going to make a lovely picnic to take with us," said Gran. "Would you like to help me, Jack?" Jack nodded. At home, he liked to help his mom, too. "Grandad likes sausage and I like cheese and tomato sandwiches," said Gran. "What's your favorite food?"

"Chocolate spread sandwiches!" said Jack, licking his lips. "Can we take something for Holly, too?"

"Of course," said Gran, smiling. "She can have one of her crunchy cookies."

When the car was clean and the picnic was ready, Jack and Grandad packed everything for their trip into the car.

Then, Gran strapped Jack into his car seat and they all set off.

"Here we are," said Grandad. "The park."

"Great!" said Jack. He couldn't wait to get out and explore. They soon found the perfect place for their picnic. Jack hungrily ate his chocolate sandwiches.

Afterwards, Grandad took Jack and Holly for a walk in the woods, while Gran had a little nap. On the way, Jack saw a playground. "Can we go there, Grandad?" he asked.

"Of course, we can," said Grandad. First, Grandad pushed Jack on the swings and then watched him zoom down the slide.

"Wheee!" cried Jack. "This is great!" Soon, he was laughing and playing with all the other children, while Grandad watched, just like Jack's mom and dad would do.

When it was time to go home, Gran packed up the picnic things and Grandad put them back in the car. Jack was very tired and soon fell asleep. What a fun day they'd had.

That evening, Gran made Jack a special dinner —sausages and mash, followed by apple pie and ice-cream.

Afterwards, they watched Jack's favorite television programes, until it was time for bed. As Jack settled himself in bed, with his teddy bear beside him, Grandad asked him what story he would like. "Mom usually reads me this one," said Jack, picking up a book and handing it to Grandad.

"Once upon a time… " began Grandad. Jack knew the story off by heart. It was nice to hear it again, and soon he was drifting off to sleep. It was just like being at home.

When Jack woke up, he couldn't understand why his room felt so strange. Then, he remembered. He was staying with Gran and Grandad!

"Breakfast, Jack," said Gran, as she came in to help him dress. "Did you sleep well?"

"Yes, thank you, Gran," he said.

For breakfast, Gran cooked Jack a boiled egg, with toast, milk, and fresh orange juice. Delicious!

Afterwards, Jack helped Gran to pack his bag, ready for when Mom and Dad came to collect him. Jack was really excited when he saw his mom and dad arrive. He ran out to meet them and gave them both a giant hug. "Jack!" cried Mom. "Have you had a good time?"

"Yes," laughed Jack. "We went to the park and had a picnic and I played on a slide and had chocolate sandwiches and we took Holly for a walk… and Grandad read me my favorite story. Can I stay again?" Everyone laughed and Holly barked.

"Of course, you can!" said Mom and Dad.

There Were Two Birds Sat on a Stone

There were two birds sat on a stone,
  Fa, la, la, la, lal, de;
One flew away, then there was one,
  Fa, la, la, la, lal, de;
The other flew after, and then there was none,
  Fa, la, la, la, lal, de;
And so the poor stone was left all alone,
  Fa, la, la, la, lal, de!

I am a Pretty Little Dutch Girl

I am a pretty little Dutch girl,
  As pretty as I can be.
And all the boys in the
  neighborhood
Are crazy over me!

Five Little Ducks

Five little ducks went swimming one day,
  Over the hills and far away,
Mother Duck said, "Quack, quack, quack, quack,"
  But only four little ducks came back.
One little duck went swimming one day,
  Over the hills and far away,
Mother Duck said, "Quack, quack, quack, quack,"
  And all the five little ducks came back.

There Was an Old Crow

There was an old crow
  Sat upon a clod:
There's an end of my song,
  That's odd!

The Wise Old Owl

There was an old owl who lived in an oak;
  The more he heard, the less he spoke.
The less he spoke, the more he heard.
  Why aren't we like that wise old bird!

The Ostrich

Here is the ostrich straight and tall,
  Nodding his head above us all.
Here is the hedgehog prickly and small,
  Rolling himself into a ball.
Here is the spider scuttling around,
  Treading so lightly on the ground.
Here are the birds that fly so high,
  Spreading their wings across the sky.
Here are the children fast asleep,
  And in the night the owls do peep,
"Tuit tuwhoo, tuit tuwhoo!"

Billy Booster

Billy Billy Booster,
  Had a little rooster,
The rooster died
  And Billy cried.
Poor Billy Booster.

Birds of a Feather

Birds of a feather flock together
  And so will pigs and swine;
Rats and mice shall have their choice,
  And so shall I have mine.

Chalk and Cheese

Chalk and Cheese were as different as two kittens can be. Chalk was a fluffy white kitten, who liked dishes of cream and lazing in the sun. Cheese was a rough, tough black kitten, who liked chewing on fish tails and climbing trees. Their mother puzzled over her odd little pair of kittens, but she loved them both the same.

One day, Cheese climbed high up on the barn and got stuck. "Help!" he cried to his sister.

"I don't like climbing!" she said, opening one eye.

"If only you were more like me!" said Cheese, "you'd be able to help!"

"If only you were more like me," said Chalk, "you wouldn't have got stuck in the first place!" And with that she went back to sleep. Just then, the farm dog came by. Chalk sprang up as he gave a loud bark and began to chase her.

"Help!" she cried to Cheese, up on the barn.

"I'm stuck, remember?" he cried. "You shouldn't lie where dogs can chase you."

Then Mommy appeared. She swiped the dog away with her claws, then climbed up and rescued Cheese.

"If only you were more like me," she said, "you'd keep out of danger and look after each other." And from then on, that's just what they did.

The Toys that Ran Away

"Put your toys away, Lucy," said Lucy's mother, "it's time for bed." Lucy gave a great big sigh. "Do I really have to?" she asked, knowing full well what the answer was going to be.

"Of course you do," said her mother. "You shouldn't have to be told to put your toys away. You really don't look after them properly."

It was true. Lucy never had been very good at looking after her toys. Once she left her beautiful new doll outside in her baby carriage and she had become ruined after it rained. Then she had carelessly dropped her tea set on the floor and some of the cups had broken. And she was forever just pushing all her toys back in the closet in a hurry, instead of putting them away carefully. Worse still, when she was in a temper, she would throw her toys, and sometimes she would even kick them.

Tonight Lucy was in another of her "can't be bothered" moods. She grabbed some dolls and a teddy and threw them into the closet. Without even looking behind her, Lucy picked up some puzzles and a skipping rope, and tossed them into the closet, too. They landed with a crash on top of the other toys. Then Lucy closed the closet door, squashing the toys even more, and went to have her bath.

Inside the toy closet Teddy said, "I'm not going to stay here a moment longer. I'm leaving for good."

"So am I!" said Katie, the ragdoll.

"I want to be somewhere where I'm not thrown around," said one of the puzzles.

One after another the toys decided they would all go back to Toyland and wait to be given to some children who would love them more.

The next morning, Lucy decided to play with some toys but, when she opened the toy closet, she couldn't believe her eyes!

All the toys had vanished. The shelves were completely empty. All day, Lucy searched high and low for her missing toys, but they were nowhere to be found. She went to bed in tears, and wondered if she would ever be able to play with her toys again.

That night, Lucy was suddenly woken by a noise in her bedroom. Was she seeing things or was that a little fairy at the bottom of her bed? "Who are you?" asked Lucy.

"I am the special messenger from Toyland," replied the fairy. "I have been sent to tell you that all your toys have run away back to Toyland, because you treated them badly."

"Oh, I do miss my toys so much," cried Lucy.

With that, the fairy floated over to Lucy, took her hand and lifted Lucy off her bed. They both flew out of Lucy's bedroom window, across fields and forests, until it became too misty to see anything at all. Then they floated down to the ground and the mist lifted, and Lucy found herself in the grounds of a huge fairy-tale castle.

"This is Toyland Castle," explained the fairy. Lucy found herself in a large, cozy room with a huge log fire. Sitting in the corner was a kindly looking little man wearing a carpenter's apron and holding a broken wooden doll. "Hello," he said, "you've come to ask your toys to return, haven't you?"

"Well… er… yes," said Lucy, not really knowing what to say.

"It's up to them to decide, of course," said the little man. "They only come back here if they are mistreated. If they are broken, I repair them, and then they go to other children who love them more."

"But I do love my toys," wept Lucy.

"Then come and tell them yourself," smiled the little man, and he led Lucy into another room. There, to her surprise, were all her toys. Not only that, but they were all shiny and new again. Nothing was broken or chipped or scratched.

Lucy ran up to her toys. "Please, toys, please come home again. I really do love you and miss you, and I promise I shall never mistreat you again," she cried, and then she hugged all the toys.

"Well, it's up to the toys now," said the little man. "You must go back home again with the fairy messenger and hope that they will give you another chance."

With that, the fairy messenger took Lucy's hand. Soon they were floating over her own yard and through her bedroom window. Lucy was so tired she fell asleep as soon as she got into bed.

In the morning she awoke, still rather sleepy, and rushed to the toy closet. There, neatly lined up on the shelves, were all her toys. Lucy was overjoyed. From that day on, she always treated her toys well and took great care of them.

Lucy never was quite sure whether the whole thing was a dream or not, but it certainly did the trick whatever it was. There was one thing that really puzzled her though. If it had just been a dream, why were all the toys so shiny and new again?

Willie Wastle

I, Willie Wastle,
  Stand on my castle,
An' a' the dogs o' your toon,
  Will no' drive Willie Wastle down.

Bow-wow

Bow-wow, says the dog,
  Mew, mew, says the cat,
Grunt, grunt, goes the hog,
  And squeak goes the rat.
Tu-whu, says the owl,
  Caw, caw, says the crow,
Quack, quack, says the duck,
  And what cuckoos say you know.

Ride Away

Ride away, ride away,
  Johnny shall ride,
He shall have a pussy cat
  Tied to one side;
He shall have a little dog
  Tied to the other,
And Johnny shall ride
  To see his grandmother.

Spin Dame

Spin, Dame, spin,
Your bread you must win;
Twist the thread and break it not,
Spin, Dame, spin.

The Robin and the Wren

The robin and the wren,
  They fought upon the porridge pan;
But before the robin got a spoon,
  The wren had eaten the porridge down.

Parliament Soldiers

High diddle ding, did you hear the bells ring?
  The parliament soldiers are gone to the king.
Some they did laugh, and some they did cry,
  To see the parliament soldiers go by.

On Oath

As I went to Bonner,
  I met a pig
Without a wig,
  Upon my word and honour.

Richard Dick

Richard Dick upon a stick,
  Sampson on a sow,
We'll ride away to Colley fair
  To buy a horse to plough.

Punctuality

Be always in time,
  Too late is a crime.

Diddlety, Diddlety

Diddlety, diddlety, dumpty,
The cat ran up the plum tree;
Half a crown to fetch her down,
Diddlety, diddlety, dumpty.

Greedy Tom

Jimmy the Mowdy
  Made a great crowdy;
Barney O'Neal
  Found all the meal;
Old Jack Rutter
  Sent two stone of butter;
The Laird of the Hot
  Boiled it in his pot;
And Big Tom of the Hall
  He supped it all.

Bless You

Bless you, bless you, burnie-bee,
  Tell me when my wedding be;
If it be tomorrow day,
Take your wings and fly away.
Fly to the east, fly to the west,
  Fly to him I love the best.

A Rat

There was a rat,
  for want of stairs,
Went down a rope
  to say his prayers.

Milking

Cushy cow, bonny, let down thy milk,
  And I will give thee a gown of silk;
A gown of silk and a silver tee,
  If thou wilt let down thy milk for me.

Missing Mouse

In some ways, Molly Mouse was just like her brother and sisters. She had soft, pink ears and a cute, little nose. But, in other ways, she was very different…

Milly, Max and Baby Mouse were very tidy, but Molly was really, really messy! Her whiskers were never clean and her paws were always grubby. And, everywhere Molly went, she left a messy muddle behind her!

After breakfast, Milly and Max never forgot to make their beds. Each and every morning, they threw out their old bedding and made new beds with fresh, clean hay. But Molly wasn't bothered! She just jumped out of bed and left everything in a tangled, untidy heap!

"How can you sleep in that mess?" asked Milly, her sister.

At lunch time, the rest of the family nibbled their food carefully and always cleaned up after themselves. They brushed up their crumbs and cleared away their bowls. But Molly wasn't bothered! She just munched away merrily, scattering food everywhere!

"Why do you make such a mess?" asked Daddy Mouse.

At playtime, Milly and Max would carefully scamper up cornstalks. But Molly couldn't be bothered! She rushed up the stalks so fast, that she snapped them in two and fell to the ground in a messy heap!

"Why are you so clumsy?" asked Max.

And when Max and Milly collected nuts and seeds for their tea, they always stacked them in neat, little piles. But Molly couldn't be bothered! Her heaps always toppled over.

"Why are you so untidy?" asked Milly.

Everyone was really fed up with Molly and her messy ways. "Why can't you eat properly?" said Daddy Mouse.

"Why can't you keep yourself clean and tidy?" said Mommy Mouse.

"Why can't you be quieter?" said Baby Mouse.

"Oh, Molly," groaned Milly and Max.

"I can't do anything right," Molly sniffed. "It's not fair." And, with her messy tail in her paw, she said "Goodnight" and went to bed.

But Molly had a plan. She was fed up with all the grumbling and she wasn't going to put up with it any longer! So, when Max and Milly came to bed, Molly was already fast asleep—at least, that's what they thought. Molly was really wide awake!

She waited until her brother and sister were asleep and then crept out of bed. "No one loves me," she sighed. "I think I'll go and find somewhere else to live." So, off she set!

Molly had no idea where she was going. She scurried along the hedgerow and scampered through the cornstalks. And, as the sun began to rise, she slipped out of the field and happily skipped down the lane.

"I'll show them!" she said. "Why should I stay at home to be grumbled and moaned at? I'm going to find a home where people want me."

But, as the morning went on and Molly got further and further away from home, she became very tired. She sat down by a farmyard gate. "I'm really sleepy," she said and gave a big yawn! Then Molly noticed the barn door slightly open. Inside was a warm and comfy pile of hay—perfect for a little nap! She snuggled up in the hay and fell fast, fast asleep.

Back at home, when Mommy Mouse came to wake up her little ones, Molly's bed was empty. "Where's Molly?" she asked Milly and Max.

The two little mice rubbed their eyes and looked around. "We don't know," they said. "She was here last night, fast asleep."

"Daddy! Daddy! Come quick!" called Mommy Mouse. "Our Molly's missing!" So, they searched the house, but Molly was not

there. They went outside and looked through the cornfield, combed the hedgerows, searched under and over toadstools, in fact, they didn't leave a leaf unturned! They even went down the lane.

Suddenly, Milly started jumping up and down. "Look!" she squealed, pointing at the muddy path that led into the farmyard.

There, right in front of Milly, was a set of tiny mouse footprints.

Milly and Max followed the footprints across the farmyard and into the barn. And there, fast asleep in a messy pile of hay, was Molly.

"We've found her!" they shouted.

Molly slowly opened her eyes. There were bits of straw sticking to her fur, her whiskers were crumpled and her paws were muddy. "Oh, Molly!" yelled Milly and Max. "We've missed you so much."

"How can you have missed *me?*" said Molly. "I'm always such a mess!"

"You might be messy," said her mommy, "but we love you just the same!" Everyone cheered and Molly smiled—they really did love her!

And with that, they set off home.

Don't be Shy Kitty

Kitty is playing with a yo-yo. "Watch me, Mom," she says. "I can make it go up and down." Suddenly, from the farmyard, Kitty hears laughing. "What is it, Mom?" she asks Cat.

"There's a big game going on," says Cat. "It looks fun, doesn't it, Kitty?"

Just then, Parsnip the pig spots Kitty. "Hello, Kitty! Come and join in!" he says. But Kitty hides behind Cat instead.

"What's the matter, Kitty?" asks Cat gently.

"The game is so loud. It makes me feel shy," Kitty says sadly.

"There's no need to be shy," says Cat. "All your friends are here."

But Kitty still feels shy. "I think I'll just watch for a bit," she says. The animals are having a wonderful time.

Then, Dennis the donkey gives the ball a big kick. "Whoops!" says Dennis. "Did anyone see where the ball went?" Quick as a flash, Kitty leaps up and races up the tree.

"I can see the ball, Mom!" she shouts. "Here it is!" Kitty laughs, throwing it down from the tree. "You're a hero, Kitty!" the animals shout. The game starts again and now Kitty is right in the middle of things.

"Great kick, Kitty," shouts Parsnip.

"You were right, Mom," she says. "I didn't need to feel shy at all."

Kitty and Cat Help Out

Kitty and Cat are going for a walk around the farm. "Look at the bees, Kitty," says Cat. "They're very busy." Suddenly Cat hears another noise. "Someone's crying," she says. "What's the matter, Little Rabbit?" asks Cat. "Why are you crying?"

"I've lost my teddy bear," sniffs Little Rabbit. "It's my favorite toy."

"Don't worry," says Kitty. "We'll help you look for it. Perhaps it's behind the haystack. I'm going to look inside the tractor," says Kitty.

"Well, I can't see your teddy," calls Kitty. "But, here's my ball of wool!"

Cat points to the gate. "Perhaps you left your teddy in the field, Little Rabbit," she says. Little Rabbit begins to cry again.

"I'll never find my teddy," he wails.

"Don't give up," says Kitty kindly. "I'm sure we'll find it soon."

"Have you looked for your teddy at home, Little Rabbit?" asks Cat. "It could be there, you know. We've looked everywhere else."

So they walk slowly to Little Rabbit's home, carefully looking for teddy on the way. But, when they arrive, they find teddy! He is tucked right down inside Little Rabbit's bed.

Little Rabbit gives Kitty a big hug. "Thank you, Kitty and Cat," he says. "I'd never have found my teddy without you!"

Birthday Bunnies

"It's my first birthday tomorrow!" announced Snowy, a little white rabbit, very proudly. "Isn't that exciting?"

"Yes, very exciting!" said Whiskers, her brother. "Because it's my birthday too!"

"And mine!" said Patch.

"And mine!" said Nibble.

"And mine!" said Twitch.

"Do you think mommy and daddy have got a surprise for us?" asked Snowy.

"I hope so!" said Whiskers, giggling.

Mrs Rabbit was listening outside the door, as her children were getting ready for bed. She heard the little bunnies chattering excitedly about their birthdays the next day.

Whatever could she do to make it a special day for them? She sat and thought very hard, and later that evening, when Mr Rabbit came home, she said: "It is the children's first birthday tomorrow, and I'm planning a surprise for them. I want to make them a carrot cake, but I will need some carrots. Could you go and dig up some nice fresh ones from your vegetable garden?"

"Certainly, dear," said Mr Rabbit, and off he went back outside.

Mr Rabbit was proud of the carrots he grew. They were very fine carrots—crunchy and delicious. Every year he entered them in the Country Show, and they nearly always won first prize. So you can imagine his dismay when he arrived at his vegetable patch to find that every single carrot had been dug up and stolen!

He marched back to the burrow. "Someone has stolen my carrots!" he told his wife, crossly. "And I am going to find out just who it is!"

And, although it was getting late, he went back outside, and set off to find the naughty person.

First of all he stopped at Hungry Hare's house, and knocked loudly.

"Someone has stolen all my carrots!" Mr Rabbit said. "Do you know who?"

"Oh, yes," said Hungry Hare. "But it wasn't me." And, although Mr Rabbit pressed him, Hungry Hare would say no more.

Next Mr Rabbit went to Sly Fox's house.

"Someone has stolen my carrots!" he said. "Do you know who?"

"Oh, yes," said Sly Fox. "But it wasn't me." And, although Mr Rabbit begged and pleaded with him, Sly Fox would say no more.

So Mr Rabbit marched to Bill Badger's house, and asked if he knew who had taken the carrots.

"Why, yes, in fact I do," said Bill Badger. "But it wasn't me."

And just like the others, he would say no more. It was the same wherever Mr Rabbit went, and, although he got very cross, and stamped his foot, no one would tell him who had stolen his carrots!

"You'll find out soon enough," said Red Squirrel.

So Mr Rabbit went home feeling very puzzled.

"It seems that everyone knows who it was, but no one will tell me!" said Mr Rabbit to his wife.

"Not everyone, dear," she said. "I don't know who it was either. All I know is that it's our children's first birthday tomorrow, and we have no surprise for them." And, feeling very miserable and confused, they went to bed, determined to get to the bottom of the mystery in the morning.

Next day the little bunnies came running into the kitchen, where their parents were having breakfast.

"Happy birthday, everyone!" called Snowy.

"Happy birthday!" cried the other little bunnies.

"Now, it's not much, but I wanted to give each of you a surprise!" Snowy went on. "By the way, I hope you don't mind, Dad." And with that Snowy pulled out a box of juicy carrots, each tied with a bow, and handed one to each of her brothers and sisters.

"Snap!" cried Whiskers, "I had just the same idea!" and he pulled out another box of carrots.

"Me too!" said Patch, and "Me too!" said Nibble. Soon there was a great pile of juicy carrots heaped on the kitchen table.

"So that's what happened to my carrots!" cried Mr Rabbit, in amazement. "I thought they had been stolen! And when he told the little bunnies the story they laughed till their sides ached. Then Mrs Rabbit put on her apron and shooed them outside.

"Just leave the carrots with me," she said. "I have a birthday surprise of my own in store!"

And so the mystery was solved. It turned out that Hungry Hare had seen the little bunnies creep out one by one, and each dig up a few carrots when they thought no one was looking. He knew it was their birthdays and he guessed what they were doing. He had told the other forest folk, and everyone thought it was a great joke.

Mr Rabbit felt very ashamed that he had been so cross with everyone, when they were really just keeping the secret. And so he invited them for a special birthday tea party that afternoon, which the little bunnies thought was a great surprise.

And of course the highlight of the day was when Mrs Rabbit appeared from the kitchen carrying, what else, but an enormous carrot cake!

One Snowy Day

One snowy day, Old Bear poked his nose out of his den, and saw the deep snow that had fallen while he slept. "I'll take a stroll in the woods," he said. Off he went, his great paws padding along, as big white snowflakes tickled his nose. How he loved the snow! He walked far into the woods, deep in thought, and quite forgot to look where he was going.

After a while, Old Bear stopped and looked around. To his dismay, he realised he was quite lost. Then he spied the trail of pawprints behind him. "Ho, ho!" he chuckled. "I'm not lost at all! I can follow my pawprints home!" And, thinking what a clever old bear he was, he carried on walking, until at last he began to feel tired. "I'll just take a rest," he said to himself. He closed his eyes, and soon fell fast asleep. Meanwhile, the snow kept on falling...

By the time Old Bear woke up his trail of pawprints had disappeared! "Now I'll never find my way home!" he groaned. Then, he noticed an old tree stump nearby.

"That looks familiar. And so does that fallen log over there. If I'm not mistaken, I've walked in a big circle, and ended up at home!" he chuckled, turning towards his den. "What a clever old bear I am, after all!"

See a Pin and Pick It Up

See a pin and pick it up,
　　All the day you'll have good luck;
See a pin and let it lay,
　　Bad luck you'll have all the day!

Miss Mary Mack

Miss Mary Mack, Mack, Mack,
　　All dressed in black, black, black,
With silver buttons, buttons, buttons,
　　All down her back, back, back.
She went upstairs to make her bed,
　　She made a mistake and bumped her head;
She went downstairs to wash the dishes,
　　She made a mistake and washed her wishes;
She went outside to hang her clothes,
　　She made a mistake and hung her nose.

Ring-a-Ring o'Roses

Ring-a-ring o'roses,
　　A pocket full of posies,
A-tishoo! A-tishoo!
　　We all fall down!

Mr Nobody

Mr Nobody is a nice young man,
　　He comes to the door with his hat in his hand.
Down she comes, all dressed in silk,
　　A rose in her bosom, as white as milk.
She takes off her gloves, she shows me her ring,
　　Tomorrow, tomorrow, the wedding begins.

Little Sally Waters

Little Sally Waters,
  Sitting in the sun,
Crying and weeping,
  For a young man.
Rise, Sally, rise,
  Dry your weeping eyes,
Fly to the east,
  Fly to the west,
Fly to the one you love the best.

Oliver Twist

Oliver Twist
  You can't do this,
So what's the use
  Of trying?
Touch your toe,
  Touch your knee,
Clap your hands,
  Away we go.

Three Children

Three children sliding on the ice
  Upon a summer's day,
As it fell out, they all fell in,
  The rest they ran away.

Now had these children been at home,
  Or sliding on dry ground,
Ten thousand pounds to one penny
  They had not all been drowned.

You parents all that children have,
  And you that have got none,
If you would have them safe abroad,
  Pray keep them safe at home.

Georgie, Porgie

Georgie, Porgie, pudding and pie,
  Kissed the girls and made them cry;
When the boys came out to play
  Georgie Porgie ran away.

A Perfect Puppy

Molly had wanted a puppy for a long time, so when Mommy and Daddy said yes, she couldn't wait to get to the pet store.

At the pet store, Polly inspected the puppies one by one. After all, her puppy had to be perfect.

"That one's too big," said Polly, pointing to a Great Dane. "And that one's too small." She pointed to a tiny Chihuahua.

"This one's nice," said the storekeeper, patting a Poodle.

"Too curly," Polly declared.

Another puppy was too noisy. And one was too quiet. Before long, there weren't many puppies left. Polly was about to give up, when something soft rubbed against her leg.

"Ah, perfect," she cried, picking up a small bundle of black and white fur.

"Err, what kind of puppy is it?" asked Daddy.

"It's my puppy," sighed Polly.

"It's a mongrel," said the storekeeper. "I think it's part Spaniel and part Collie. We're not really sure."

"I don't care what he is," smiled Polly. "He's just perfect. I'm going to call him Danny."

A PERFECT PUPPY

Danny whined as he left the pet store. And he whined all the way home. He stopped whining when he saw the cat and barked instead.

"He'll be okay once he gets used to us," said Mommy. Polly hoped she was right.

In the afternoon, they took Danny for a walk. Polly took some bread to feed the ducks, but as soon as Danny saw the ducks he started to bark. Then he began to chase them and didn't stop until they had all flown away.

Daddy bought Polly an ice-cream to cheer her up.

"He's just a puppy. He's got a lot to learn," explained Daddy as Danny jumped up and stole her ice cream. Polly was beginning to wonder if she'd chosen the right puppy.

When they got home, Polly decided to introduce Danny to all her dolls and cuddly toys, but Danny pounced on her favorite teddy.

"He's got Mr Fluffy," cried Polly, as Danny raced from the room into the yard. When he came back, Mr Fluffy was gone.

Polly was furious. She waved an angry finger at Danny. "You're not a perfect puppy," she said. "I don't think you'll ever learn."

Poor Danny, he hung his head and slunk away under the table and wouldn't come out all evening.

The next morning, Polly was woken up by something wet pressed against her cheek. It was Danny, and in his mouth was Mr Fluffy! Danny dropped Mr Fluffy on the floor for Polly to pick up.

"Good boy, Danny," laughed Polly, tickling his ears. "You are a perfect puppy, after all!"

The Red Daffodil

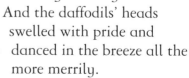

It was spring time and all the daffodils were pushing their heads up towards the warmth of the sun. Slowly, their golden petals unfolded to let their yellow trumpets dance in the breeze. One particular field of daffodils was a blaze of gold like all the others—but right in the middle was a single splash of red. For there in the middle was a red daffodil.

From the moment she opened her petals, the red daffodil knew she was different from the other flowers. They sneered at her and whispered to each other. "What a strange, poor creature!" said one.

"She must envy our beautiful golden color," said another.

And indeed it was true. The red daffodil wished very much that she was like the others. Instead of being proud of her red petals, she was ashamed and hung her head low. "What's wrong with me?" she thought. "Why aren't there any other red daffodils in the field?"

Passers-by stopped to admire the field of beautiful daffodils. "What a wonderful sight!" they exclaimed. And the daffodils' heads swelled with pride and danced in the breeze all the more merrily.

Then someone spotted the red daffodil right in the middle

of the field. "Look at that extraordinary flower!" the man shouted. Everyone peered into the centre of the field.

"You're right," said someone else, "there's a red daffodil in the middle." Soon a crowd had gathered, all pointing at the red daffodil.

She could feel herself blushing even redder at the attention. "How I wish my petals would close up again," she said to herself in anguish. But, try as she might, her fine red trumpet stood out for all to see.

Now, in the crowd of people gathered at the edge of the field was a little girl. People were pushing and shoving and she couldn't see anything at all. At last, her father lifted her high upon his shoulders so that she could see into the field. "Oh!" exclaimed the little girl in a very big voice. "So that's the red daffodil. I think it's really beautiful. What a lucky daffodil to be so different."

And, do you know, other people heard what the little girl said and they began to whisper to each other, "Well, I must say, I actually thought myself it was rather pretty, you know." Before long, people were praising the daffodil's beauty and saying it must be a very special flower. The red daffodil heard what the crowd was saying. Now she was blushing with pride and held her head as high as all the other daffodils in the field.

The other daffodils were furious. "What a foolish crowd," said one indignantly. "We are the beautiful ones!" They turned their heads away from the red daffodil and ignored her. She began to feel unhappy again.

By now word had spread far and wide about the amazing red daffodil and people came from all over the land to see her.

Soon, the king's daughter got to hear about the red daffodil. "I must see this for myself," said the princess. She set off with her servants and eventually they came to the field where the red daffodil grew. When the princess saw her, she clapped her hands and jumped up and down with excitement.

"The red daffodil is more beautiful than I ever imagined," she cried. Then she had an idea. "Please bring my pet dove," she said to her servant. The man looked rather puzzled, but soon he returned with the bird. "As you know," said the princess to the servant, "I am to be married tomorrow and I would dearly love to have that red daffodil in my wedding bouquet."

The princess sent the dove into the middle of the field and it gently picked up the daffodil in its beak and brought her back to where the princess stood. The princess carried the daffodil back to the palace. She put the daffodil in a vase of water and there she stayed until the next day.

In the morning, the princess's servant took the red daffodil to the church. The daffodil could hear the bells and see all the guests assembling for the wedding ceremony. Then she saw the princess arrive in a wonderful coach pulled by four white horses.

How lovely the princess looked in her beautiful gown and her head crowned with deep red roses.

As the servant reached the church door, the princess's lady-in-waiting stepped forward holding a huge bouquet of flowers. Just as the flowers were handed to the princess the servant placed the red daffodil among the other flowers in the bouquet. For a while, the red daffodil was overcome by the powerful scents of the other flowers in the bouquet, but when at last she looked around her she realised, with astonishment, that all of them were red. There were red daisies, red lilies, red carnations and red foxgloves. "Welcome," said one of the daisies, "you're one of us." And, for the first time in her life, the red daffodil felt really at home.

After the wedding, the princess scattered the flowers from her bouquet among the flowers in her yard. Every spring, when she opened her petals, the red daffodil found she was surrounded by lots of other red flowers, and she lived happily in the yard for many, many years.

As I was Going to St Ives

As I was going to St Ives,
  I met a man with seven wives.
Each wife had seven sacks,
  Each sack had seven cats,
Each cat had seven kits.
  Kits, cats, sacks, and wives,
How many were going to St Ives?

The Little Turtle Dove

High in the pine tree,
  The little turtle dove
Made a little nursery
  To please her little love.

"Coo," said the turtle dove,
  "Coo," said she;
In the long, shady branches
  Of the dark pine tree.

Dickery Dickery Dare

Dickery, dickery dare,
  The pig flew up in the air.
The man in brown
  Soon brought him down!
Dickery, dickery, dare.

Hey, my Kitten

Hey, my kitten, my kitten,
  And hey my kitten, my deary,
Such a sweet pet as this
  There is not far not neary.
Here we go up, up, up,
  Here we go down, down, downy;
Here we go backwards and fowards,
  And here we go round, round, roundy.

Pussycat Ate the Dumplings

Clap Hands

Clap hands, Daddy's coming
  Up the waggon way,
His pockets full of money
  And his hands full of clay.

Pussycat ate the dumplings,
  Pussycat ate the dumplings,
Mamma stood by,
  And cried, "Oh fie!
Why did you eat the dumplings?"

There Was...

There was a girl
   in our town,
Silk an' satin was
   her gown,
Silk an' satin, gold an'
   velvet.
Guess her name, three
   times I've telled it.

The Mischievous Raven

A farmer went trotting upon his gray mare,
   Bumpety, bumpety, bump!
With his daughter behind him so rosy and fair,
   Lumpety, lumpety, lump!

A raven cried, "Croak!" and they all tumbled down,
   Bumpety, bumpety, bump!
The mare broke her knees and the farmer his crown,
   Lumpety, lumpety, lump!

The mischievous raven flew laughing away,
   Bumpety, bumpety, bump!
And vowed he would serve them the same next day,
   Lumpety, lumpety, lump!

Cats and Dogs

Hodley, poddley, puddle and fogs,
   Cats are to marry the poodle dogs;
Cats in blue jackets and dogs in red hats,
   What will become of the mice and the rats?

I Bought an Old Man

Hey diddle diddle,
   And hey diddle dan!
And with a little money,
   I bought an old man.
His legs were all crooked
   And wrong ways set on,
So what do you think
   Of my little old man?

Mrs White

Mrs White had a fright
   In the middle of the night.
She saw a ghost, eating toast,
   Halfway up a lamp post.

The New Arrival

All day long, Old MacDonald's cows grazed in the green meadow and chatted. Nothing happened on the farm that Poppy, Annabel, Emily and Heather didn't know about.

One morning Old MacDonald visited the horses in the field next door.

"Here's an apple for you and George, Tilly," he said. "I wanted you to be the first to hear—we're expecting a new baby on the farm. You can imagine Mrs MacDonald is very excited about it because..."

But, before he could finish, there was the sound of thundering hooves from the field next to them as a cow, bursting with news, dashed off to find her friends.

"Are you sure?" mooed Annabel, as Poppy panted out what she had heard.

"Positive," gasped Poppy.

"Old MacDonald and Mrs MacDonald, aren't they, well, a bit old to be having a baby?" asked Emily.

"Yes, I thought that," said Poppy. "But I heard it from Old MacDonald himself."

"But if Mrs MacDonald has a baby to look after," said Heather, "who will give me my beauty treatments before the Country Show? I simply must win a rosette again this year."

There was silence. Then Annabel said what the animals had all been thinking.

"Ladies! This news is far too important to keep to ourselves! We must tell the others immediately!" And off the four cows dashed.

So, leaning over the gate, Emily mumbled to Jenny the hen. "What?" she squawked. "If Mrs MacDonald has a baby to look after, who is going to collect my eggs? I will tell Henry!"

Henry the rooster crowed when he heard the news. "Well, cock-a-doodle-doo!" he cried. "If Mrs MacDonald has a baby to look after, who will throw me my corn to peck?" So Henry hurried off to talk to Debbie the duck.

And so it went on. Debbie told Milly the cat, who told Percy the pig, who told Bruce the farm dog. And Bruce scampered off to tell Maria and the rest of the sheep.

By lunch time, every animal on the farm was worried. Things simply wouldn't be the same if Mrs MacDonald was looking after a baby. In fact, the animals were all so busy and bothered, they didn't notice a truck pulling into the farmyard.

"The new arrival!" called Old MacDonald.

"What, already?" squawked Jenny. "But I thought… oh!"

Out of the truck trotted a beautiful little foal, a new friend for Tilly and Old George.

"It's so lovely to have another baby animal on the farm!" cried Mrs MacDonald.

She was too excited to hear the sigh of relief from all the animals, or the mooing from the meadow, as the other cows had a few well-chosen words with Poppy!

Baby Bear finds a Friend

Baby Bear stretched as he woke from his long, winter sleep. He took a deep breath of fresh spring air and smiled at the warm sun on his back. He was bursting with energy. Now he needed someone to play with.

"Come and play with me," he called to Owl.

"I only play at night!" said Owl, sleepily.

Nearby some little bunnies were playing. Baby Bear bounded over to join the fun, but Mrs Rabbit shooed him off. "Your paws will hurt my babies," she said. "You can't play with them."

Baby Bear wandered down to the river, where some beavers were hard at work building a dam. "Come and play with me," called Baby Bear.

But the beavers were too busy. So he sat watching Kingfisher diving into the water.

"That looks like fun!" he said, jumping in with a splash!

"Go away!" said Kingfisher. "You will disturb the fish!"

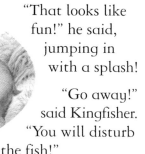

By now Baby Bear was feeling fed up and tired. He lay down in a hollow and closed his eyes. Then, just as he was drifting to sleep, a voice said, "Will you come and play with me?" He opened his eyes to see another bear cub. Baby Bear smiled. "I'm too tired to play now," he said. "But I'll play with you tomorrow!" And from then on, he was never lonely again.

Three Little Kittens

Three little kittens they lost their mittens,
  And they began to cry,
Oh, mother dear, we sadly fear
  That we have lost our mittens.

What! lost your mittens, you naughty kittens!
  Then you shall have no pie.
Mee-ow, mee-ow, mee-ow.
  No, you shall have no pie.

The three little kittens they found their mittens,
  And they began to cry,
Oh, mother dear, see here, see here,
  For we have found our mittens.

Put on your mittens, you silly kittens,
  And you shall have some pie.
Purr-r, purr-r, purr-r,
  Oh, let us have some pie.

Gee Up, Neddy

Gee up, Neddy,
  Don't you stop,
Just let your feet go
  Clippety clop.
Clippety clopping,
  Round and round.
Giddy up,
  We're homeward bound.

Hark! Hark!

Hark, hark,
  The dogs do bark,
Beggars are coming to town:
  Some in rags,
Some in tags,
  And some in velvet gowns.

Slowly, Slowly

Slowly, slowly, very slowly
  Creeps the garden snail.

Slowly, slowly, very slowly
  Up the garden rail.

Quickly, quickly, very quickly
  Runs the little mouse.

Quickly, quickly, very quickly
  Round about the house.

A Cat Came Fiddling

A cat came fiddling out of a barn,
  With a pair of bagpipes under her arm;
She could sing nothing but fiddle cum fee,
  The mouse has married the humble-bee.
Pipe, cat—dance, mouse,
  We'll have a wedding at our good house.

There Was a Little Turtle

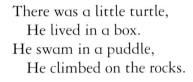

There was a little turtle,
  He lived in a box.
He swam in a puddle,
  He climbed on the rocks.

He snapped at a mosquito,
  He snapped at a flea.
He snapped at a minnow,
  He snapped at me.

He caught the mosquito,
  He caught the flea.
He caught the minnow,
  But… he didn't catch me!

The Little Bird

This little bird flaps its wings,
  Flaps its wings, flaps its wings,
This little bird flaps its wings,
  And flies away in the morning!

As Small as a Mouse

As small as a mouse,
  As wide as a bridge,
As tall as a house,
  As straight as a pin.

The Magic Tree

Tommy rubbed his eyes, blinked hard, and looked out of his bedroom window again. But it was still there—an enormous oak tree that definitely hadn't been there yesterday! If it had been there, he'd have known all about it for sure. For a start he would have climbed up it, for Tommy loved nothing better than climbing trees.

No, this tree was definitely not there yesterday! Tommy sat staring at the tree in wonder and disbelief. The tree stood there, outside his bedroom window, with its huge, spreading branches almost asking to be climbed. Tommy wondered how on earth it had suddenly got there, but he decided that, before he wondered about that too much, he had better go and climb it first. After all, there was always time later to wonder about things but never enough time to do things, he thought.

As soon as he was dressed, he ran outside to take a closer look at the new tree. It seemed just like any other big oak tree. It had lots of wide, inviting branches and lots of green, rounded leaves. And it had deep, furrowed bark just like any other oak tree.

Tommy couldn't resist any longer—he began to climb. In no time at all, he was in a green, leafy canopy. He couldn't see the ground any more, but something was not quite right. The branches beneath his feet seemed to be so big that he could stand up on them and walk in any direction. And the branches around him were just like trees themselves. In fact, he suddenly realised that he wasn't climbing a tree any longer, but standing in a whole forest full of trees.

Tommy thought he had better get down. But where was down? All he could see were tall, swaying trees with twisty paths leading off even deeper into the forest. Tommy didn't know how he had done it, but he had got himself lost in a forest, and he hadn't even had breakfast yet!

Worse still, it seemed to be getting dark. "Quick, over here!" a voice suddenly called out. Tommy was very startled, but he was even more startled when he saw that the voice belonged to a squirrel.

"You can speak!" blurted out Tommy.

"Of course I can speak!" snapped the squirrel. "Now listen. You are in great danger, and there's no time to lose if we are to save you from the clutches of the evil Wizard of the Woods."

The squirrel quickly explained that, long ago, a spell had been cast on the forest and it had become enchanted. Every now and again, the

Wizard of the Woods lured an unsuspecting person into his realm by making a tree appear. Once you climbed the tree, you entered the forest. Escape was almost impossible.

"But why does the Wizard of the Woods want to lure people into the forest?" asked Tommy, knowing that he wouldn't like the answer.

"To turn them into fertiliser to make the trees grow," said the squirrel.

Tommy didn't really know what fertiliser was, but it sounded nasty. He was pleased when the squirrel suddenly said, "There is just one way to get you out of here. But we must hurry. Soon it will be dark and the Wizard of the Woods will awake. Once he awakes, he will smell your blood and he will capture you."

Jumping up the nearest tree, the squirrel called, "Follow me."

Tommy immediately climbed after the squirrel. "Where are we going?" he panted as they climbed higher and higher.

"To the top of the tallest tree in the forest," the squirrel answered as they clambered from tree to tree, climbing ever higher. "It's the only way to escape. You'll see!" said the squirrel.

Eventually they stopped climbing. Below them and around them was nothing but more trees. Tommy looked up, and at last he could see the clear, twilight sky. He also noticed something rather strange. All the leaves at the top of the tallest tree were enormous.

"Quick, time is running out," said the squirrel. "Sit on this leaf and hold tight."

Tommy sat on one of the huge leaves. The squirrel whistled, and before Tommy could blink he had been joined by a hundred more squirrels. They each took hold of the branch to which the leaf was attached. With a great heave, they pulled and pulled until the branch was bent backwards. Suddenly they let go. With a mighty "TWANG", the branch, with Tommy and the leaf attached, sprang forward. As it did so Tommy and the leaf were launched into the air. High above the trees they soared until, ever so slowly, they began to float down to earth. Down, down, they went, until they landed with a bump.

Tommy opened his eyes to find himself on his bedroom floor. He ran over to the window and looked out. The magic tree was nowhere to be seen. It had gone as quickly as it had appeared—perhaps it had never been there at all. Perhaps it had just been a dream... What do you think?

The Spooks' Ball

It is midnight and the spooks are going to the Annual Ball in the old Haunted Hall. By the light of the moon they will dance to a band that will play terrible tunes all night.

A spooks' band has instruments the like of which you will never have seen! The drums are made from skulls of all different shapes and sizes, the piano is made from the teeth of a dinosaur, and the violin is played with a bow made from cats' whiskers. But the strangest sound comes from the skeletons when they take to the dance floor. They shake their bones in time to the band, making a rattling tune which makes them howl with glee! In amongst the shaking skeletons is a witch dancing with her cat, but her boots are so big that she can't keep up with everyone else! A ghost with his head tucked underneath his arm is slowly feeding himself chips.

As the sun rises the spooks all fade away and the Ball is over for another year—or have you been dreaming?

The Haunted House

Have you ever been in a haunted house? No? Well, follow me and I will take you on a guided tour...

Step carefully through the rusty gates, but be quiet as a mouse, you don't want to upset the residents. Open the front door very slowly—otherwise it will creak and squeak, then everyone will know we are here. The hallway is full of ghosts wafting backwards and forwards, and look... some are walking through the doors when they are closed!

There are ghastly ghouls lurking on the stairs, and imps and sprites are having pillow fights. Look out—you will get covered in feathers!

Push open the kitchen door and a wizard is making slug and spider pies. I don't think we will stay to sample those when they are ready to come out of the oven!

Upstairs, skeletons are getting dressed and vampires are brushing their teeth. A suit of armor is about to get in the bathtub—we won't stay in case he goes rusty!

So, an ordinary day in a haunted house—would you like to move in?

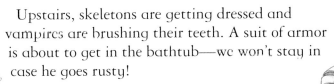

Beauty and the Beast

Once upon a time there was a man who lived in a cottage in the country with his three daughters. His youngest daughter was so pretty that everyone called her "Beauty", which made her two sisters very angry and jealous.

One day the man had to go to the city. Before he left, he told his daughters that he would bring each of them back a present and asked what they would like.

"Jewels!" the eldest daughter demanded. "Silk dresses!" said the second daughter. But all Beauty asked for was a single white rose.

On his return home, the father was caught in a snowstorm and lost his way. The blizzard was so thick and fierce, and the forest so large and dark, that he nearly gave up hope of ever finding his home. Then, through the mist, he glimpsed a grand palace.

He staggered to the great door—there seemed to be no one about. Inside, he found

236

a table laid with a magnificent dinner. The man ate hungrily, then searched the house. Upstairs, he found a huge bed where he gratefully fell into an exhausted sleep. In the morning, when he awoke, breakfast was waiting beside the bed.

As he set off on his way home he noticed a wonderful rose garden. Remembering Beauty's request, he stopped to pick a white rose. Suddenly, with a mighty roar, a terrifying, snarling Beast appeared.

"I have welcomed you with every comfort," he growled, "and in return you steal my roses!"

Shaking with fear, the man begged for forgiveness. "I only wanted the rose as a present for my daughter!"

"I will spare you," said the Beast, "but only if your daughter comes to live here of her own free will. If not, you must return in three months."

Back home, the man tearfully told his daughters what had happened. To his surprise, Beauty agreed to go.

When she arrived at the palace, a glorious meal was waiting for her.

"The Beast must want to fatten me," she thought. But she sat and ate.

As soon as Beauty finished her meal, the Beast appeared. He was truly horrifying, and she was frightened.

"Your room is all ready," said the Beast, and he led her to a door that said "Beauty's Room" in gold letters.

The room was everything Beauty could have wished for. She saw a little piano, beautiful silk dresses and fresh, fragrant roses. On the dressing table was a mirror with these words on it:

If anything you long to see,
Speak your wish, and look in me.

"I wish I could see my father," said Beauty, and instantly saw her father in the mirror, sitting sadly beside the fire at home.

"Perhaps the Beast doesn't mean to kill me after all," Beauty thought. "I wonder what he does want?"

The next evening the Beast joined Beauty for supper. "Tell me," he said, "am I truly horrible to look at?"

Beauty could not lie. "You are," she said. "But I know you are very kind-hearted."

"Then," said the Beast, "will you marry me?"

Beauty was surprised. She knew he might be angry if she refused, but she couldn't say yes because she didn't love him. "No," she said, "I will not marry you."

The Beast sighed so heavily that the walls shook. "Good night, then," he said sadly. And he left her to finish her dinner alone.

Months passed, and the Beast gave Beauty everything she could want. She was very happy in the palace.

Every evening, the Beast asked the same question: "Will you marry me?" And Beauty always said no. But she was growing very fond of him.

One day, Beauty looked in the magic mirror and saw that her father was ill. She begged the Beast to let her go home, and sadly he agreed.

"Take this magic ring," he told her. "If you ever want to come back, put it by your bedside, and when you wake up, you will be here."

"I will come back," Beauty promised.

So Beauty went home to look after her father. He was soon well again, and she was ready to go back to the Beast. But her jealous sisters hated to think of Beauty going back to a palace while they lived in a small cottage. So they convinced her to stay a while longer.

One night, Beauty dreamt that the Beast was lying dead in his garden, and she woke up in tears. She knew then that she loved the Beast, and had to return to him.

Putting the magic ring by her bedside, Beauty lay down again and closed her eyes.

When she opened them again, Beauty was back in the Beast's garden—and, true to her dream, he was lying lifeless on the ground.

"Oh, Beast," she cried, taking him in her arms, "please don't die! I love you, and I want to marry you!"

All at once light and music filled the air, and the Beast vanished. In his place stood a handsome prince.

"Who are you?" cried Beauty.

"I was your Beast," said the prince. "An evil witch cast a spell on me and turned me into that poor animal. The spell could only be broken when a beautiful girl agreed to marry me."

A few days later they were married, and Beauty's family came to join in the joyous celebrations at the palace.

Beauty had never been so happy. She loved the prince with all her heart, and they lived in their rose palace happily ever after.

Ballerina Belle

Belle the ballerina is a beautiful ballet dancer. She loves to dance in her frilly tutu and satin ballet shoes. She has a best friend—Pearl, a fluffy white kitten with big blue eyes. Pearl enjoys watching Belle dance, spinning and twirling across the floor.

Today Belle is getting ready for a very special show. The little kitten sits on her friend's pink dressing table. purring with delight, as Belle carefully dusts a sprinkling of powder over her face.

Belle is so excited and nervous. Tonight, she will dance for the King and Queen.

BALLERINA BELLE

Pearl purrs her approval as the little ballerina puts on a blue tutu that glistens with jewels. Then she ties the pretty ribbons on her shoes. Finally, Belle puts up her lovely long hair with silver hairpins. Pearl thinks she looks wonderful. Now Belle is all ready for the show and tiptoes to the stage…

The music starts and Belle begins to twirl gracefully across the floor. The King and Queen love to watch her dance—she is the most beautiful ballerina ever.

As the audience cheers, Pearl purrs with delight. Belle's the happiest ballerina in the world.

The Snake

A narrow fellow in the grass
    Occasionally rides;
You may have met him—did you not?
    His notice sudden is.

The grass divides as with a comb,
    A spotted shaft is seen;
And then it closes at your feet
    And opens further on.

He likes a boggy acre,
    A floor too cool for corn.
Yet when a child, and barefoot,
    I more than once, at morn,

    Have passed, I thought, a whip-lash
        Unbraiding in the sun—
    When, stooping to secure it,
        It wrinkled, and was gone.

EMILY DICKINSON

Calico Pie

Calico Pie,
    The little Birds fly
Down to the calico tree,
    Their wings were blue,
And they sang "Tilly-loo!"
    Till away they flew—
And they never came back to me!
    They never came back!
They never came back!
    They never came back to me!

Calico Jam,
    The little Fish swam,
Over the syllabub sea,
    He took off his hat,
To the Sole and the Sprat,
    And the Willeby-wat—
But he never came back to me!
    He never came back!
He never came back!
    He never came back to me!

Caterpillar

Brown and furry
    Caterpillar in a hurry,
Take your walk
    To the shady leaf, or stalk,
Or what not,
    Which may be the chosen spot.

No toad spy you,
    Hovering bird of prey pass by you;
Spin and die,
    To live again a butterfly.

The Cow

The friendly cow all red and white,
  I love with all my heart:
She gives me cream with all her might,
  To eat with apple-tart.

She wanders lowing here and there,
  And yet she cannot stray,
All in the pleasant open air,
  The pleasant light of day.

And blown by all the winds that pass
  And wet with all the showers,
She walks among the meadow grass
  And eats the meadow flowers.

To a Butterfly

I've watched you now a full half-hour,
  Self-poised upon that yellow flower;
And, little Butterfly! indeed
  I know not if you sleep or feed.
How motionless! ——not frozen seas
  More motionless! And then
What joy awaits you, when the breeze
  Hath found you out among the trees,
And calls you forth again!

This plot of orchard-ground is ours;
  My trees they are, my Sister's flowers.
Here rest your wings when they are weary;
  Here lodge as in a sanctuary!
Come often to us, fear no wrong;
  Sit near us on the bough!
We'll talk of sunshine and of song,
  And summer days, when we were young;
Sweet childish days, that were as long
  As twenty days are now.

The Fairies

Up the airy mountain,
  Down the rushy glen,
We daren't go a-hunting
  For fear of little men;
Wee folk, good folk,
  Trooping all together;
Green jacket, red cap,
  And white owl's feather!

Down along the rocky shore
  Some make their home;
They live on crispy pancakes
  Of yellow tide-foam;
Some in the reeds
  Of the black mountain lake,
With frogs for their watch-dogs,
  All night awake.

Monty the Mongrel

Monty was a very curious puppy. He liked nothing better than exploring the garden.

"Don't go far," Mommy would say. But Monty wasn't worried about getting lost. He was a very good explorer.

One day, a big truck pulled up outside the house where Monty and his family lived. Men began carrying things out of the house. One of them said something about moving, but Monty was just a puppy and didn't know what that meant.

One of the men left the gate open so, when no one was looking, Monty crept out and he had a wonderful time sniffing around other people's yards. He found lots of yummy things to eat. And some really lovely things to roll in.

After a while, Monty began to feel tired. He was such a good explorer that he sniffed his way home with no trouble.

But when he got there, he couldn't believe his eyes. Everyone, including Mommy and all his brothers and sisters, had gone.

Monty was very surprised but he wasn't too worried. After all, he was a very good explorer. He began sniffing at once.

He soon found himself in the park where he met a group of dogs.

"Who are you?" asked one, and, "What are you?" asked another.

"Well, he's not a Poodle," sniffed the first dog, who Monty couldn't help thinking looked like a ball of cotton wool. "He's far too rough."

"He's definitely not a Dachshund," said another dog.

"He's certainly not an Old English Sheepdog," barked a third dog. "He's just not hairy enough."

"Hmm!" grunted a fourth dog, who had the flattest nose Monty had ever seen. He walked around Monty and stared at him from all sides. Then he stopped and shuddered. "Do you know what I think? I think he's a MONGREL."

"Well, if that's the case," sniffed the cotton wool dog, "he'd better hang out with Tinker."

"Take no notice of them," said Tinker. "They're just trying to help."

Monty gave Tinker a lick, and before long he was telling Tinker about his family.

"Let's walk around the park," said Tinker. "If we follow our noses, we might find your family."

In the park, Monty sniffed the air. He could smell a very familiar smell. Then, he heard a very familiar bark. Suddenly, a huge brown dog bounded out of one of the houses on the other side of the park.

"Run for your lives," yelped the cotton wool dog.

"Help! It's a giant," barked the flat-nosed dog.

"Mommy!" shouted Monty.

"Monty!" barked Mommy. "Thank goodness you're safe."

"So you're a Great Dane puppy," laughed Tinker. "Not a mongrel, after all."

The Good Old Days

O n cold, wet and windy afternoons, when Old MacDonald lets his animals shelter in the warm barn, they like listening to stories. But, it does depend who's telling the story!

The pigs tell tales about food. The hens' stories usually concern the ducks, and the cows are terrible gossips—they repeat things they have half-heard over the hedge!

But Old George and Tilly, the oldest animals on the farm, always talk about how much better it was in days gone by. This bores the other animals. They have heard them many times before.

One very cold spring day the farm was full of newborn chicks.

Old MacDonald went to the henhouse and told Henrietta, "Take your babies into the barn. It will be much cosier there than in here."

"Baaa!" bleated Maria the sheep, who was standing near the barn door. "Did you hear that? Henrietta is bringing her chicks in. There'll be no peace now!"

Suddenly, there was mooing, neighing, snorting and quacking as the other animals all agreed. Those tiny chicks were the most troublesome little creatures on the farm. And the animals all stared in dismay as, one by one, the chicks filed in.

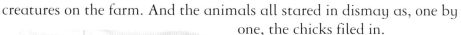

It was Percy the pig's turn to tell a story. "Once upon a time," he began, "there lived a pig who was very hungry…"

Although the animals tried to concentrate, the lively little chicks made it difficult to listen. They pecked at Heather the cow's nose, making her sneeze. They scratched at Bruce the farm dog's tail until he was forced to bark quite sharply at them. One chick even tried to go to sleep in Maria the sheep's wooly ear. It was very distracting and it made all the animals cross.

"… something very, very delicious. The end," said Percy, aware that no one had been able to listen to his story. He oinked loudly at the chicks and stomped off into a corner to sulk.

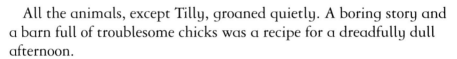

Next, it was Old George the horse's turn. "My tale," he said, "is about the good old days…"

All the animals, except Tilly, groaned quietly. A boring story and a barn full of troublesome chicks was a recipe for a dreadfully dull afternoon.

However, as Old George droned on and on and on, an amazing thing happened. Each and every chirping chick began to fall asleep snug in the warmth of Henrietta's feathers.

"… and that reminds me of another story," said Old George, "but I don't expect you want to hear that today."

"Oh, yes! Yes, we do!" chorused the other animals. "We love your stories, George!" And this time they meant every word of it!

Oh Dear, What Can the Matter Be?

Oh dear, what can the matter be?
  Dear, dear, what can the matter be?
Oh dear, what can the matter be?
  Johnny's so long at the fair.

He promised he'd buy me a basket of posies,
  A garland of lilies, a garland of roses,
A little straw hat to set off the blue ribbons
  That tie up my bonny brown hair.

Oh dear, what can the matter be?
  Dear, dear, what can the matter be?
Oh dear, what can the matter be?
  Johnny's so long at the fair.

Goosey Goosey Gander

Goosey, goosey, gander,
  Whither shall I wander?
Upstairs and downstairs,
  And in my lady's chamber.
There I met an old man
  Who would not say his prayers,
I took him by the left leg
  And threw him down the stairs

Knick Knack Paddy Whack

This old man, he played one,
  He played knick knack on my drum.
With a knick knack paddy whack, give a dog a bone,
  This old man went rolling home.

This old man, he played two,
  He played knick knack on my shoe.
With a knick knack paddy whack, give a dog a bone,
  This old man went rolling home.

Jack and Jill

Jack and Jill went up the hill
　To fetch a pail of water;
Jack fell down and broke his crown
　And Jill came tumbling after.

Up Jack got and home did trot
　As fast as he could caper;
He went to bed to mend his head
　With vinegar and brown paper.

Cock-a-Doodle-Doo

Cock-a-doodle-doo!
　My dame has lost her shoe,
My master's lost his fiddling stick,
　And doesn't know what to do.

Cock-a-doodle-doo!
　What is my dame to do?
Till master finds his fiddling stick,
　She'll dance without her shoe.

Cock-a-doodle-doo!
　My dame has found her shoe,
And master's found his fiddling stick,
　Sing cock-a-doodle-doo!

Girls and Boys Come Out to Play

Girls and boys, come out to play;
　The moon doth shine as bright as day;
Leave your supper, and leave your sleep,
　And come with your playfellows into the street.

Come with a whoop, come with a call,
　Come with a good will or not at all.
Up the ladder and down the wall,
　A halfpenny roll will serve us all.
You find milk, and I'll find flour,
　And we'll have a pudding in half-an-hour.

The Clumsy Fairy

Did you know that all fairies have to go to school to learn how to be fairies? They have to learn how to fly, how to be graceful and how to do magic. Clementine found it difficult! Poor Clementine. She was the worst in the class. She was clumsy and awkward. When they were dancing she was the only fairy who tripped over her own feet.

"Clementine! Think of feathers, not elephants," Madam Bouquet, the fairy dance teacher, was forever saying. At the end of the semester all the fairies were given a special task for the holidays. But there was one task that no one wanted. This was to help a little girl who had measles.

"Clementine," said Madam Bouquet, "I want you to paint this rose petal lotion on the little girl's spots every night when she is asleep," said Madam Bouquet. "If you do this for one week, the spots will disappear."

That night Clementine flew in through the little girl's window. So far so good! The little girl's name was Alice, and Clementine could see her fast asleep in bed. She was holding a fat, round teddy in her arms.

Clementine crept towards the bed. Then a toy clown, with a silly face, pinched her behind! "Ouch!" she yelled.

Alice woke up. "Who's there?" she asked sleepily.

"It's Clementine," said the fairy. "Your clown pinched my behind!"

Then Clementine overbalanced and sat down quickly on Alice's hot water bottle which was lying on the floor. It was so bouncy she shot straight up in the air and landed with a plop on Alice's bed.

"Are you alright?" asked Alice, rubbing her eyes again, to make sure she wasn't seeing things.

Clementine explained to Alice why she had come. "I'm sorry I woke you," she added. "You're not really supposed to see me."

Alice didn't mind. It was lovely to be able to talk to a real fairy. "Can you really do magic?" she asked Clementine.

"Yes," Clementine told her. "I'm quite good at magic. I just wish I wasn't so clumsy." She told Alice about her dance classes and Alice told Clementine about her ballet lessons.

"If you are helping me get rid of my measles," she said to Clementine, "I'll help you with your ballet." Each night Alice taught Clementine how to point her toes, keep her balance on one foot and curtsy gracefully. But it was the pirouette that Clementine did best of all. Holding her arms high above her head she twirled and twirled round Alice's bedroom.

Each day Clementine painted Alice's spots and by the end of the week they had gone.

After the vacation the fairies went back to school. And, do you know, Clementine was the best dancer in the class! Madam Bouquet couldn't believe her eyes.

"Why, Clementine," she gasped, "you're my prima ballerina!" And "prima", as I'm sure you know, means "first and best"!

Clementine was the happiest fairy in the world!

Wobbly Bear

Mr and Mrs Puppety owned an old-fashioned toy store. They made toys by hand in a room at the back of the store. But they were getting old and their eyesight was bad.

"It's time we got an apprentice toymaker," said Mr Puppety to his wife. They soon found a young man called Tom to work for them. He worked hard and carefully. He spent his first week making a teddy bear. When he had finished he showed the bear to Mr and Mrs Puppety.

"He looks very cuddly," said Mrs Puppety.

Tom was pleased that they liked his bear and he went off home whistling happily.

"He really is a lovely bear," said Mr Puppety, "but his head is a bit wobbly."

"I know," said his wife, "but it's Tom's first try. Let's just put him up there on the shelf with the other teddy bears."

That night Wobbly Bear sat on the shelf and started to cry. He had heard what Mr and Mrs Puppety had said about him.

"What's wrong?" asked Brown Bear, who was sitting next to him.

"My head is on wobbly," sobbed Wobbly Bear.

"Does it hurt?" asked Brown Bear.

"No," replied Wobbly Bear.

"Well then, why are you crying?" asked Brown Bear.

"Because nobody will want to buy a wobbly bear. I'll be left in this store forever and nobody will ever take me home and love me," he cried.

"Don't worry," said Brown Bear. "We've all got our faults, and you look fine to me. Just try your best to look cute and cuddly and you'll soon have someone to love you." This made Wobbly Bear feel much happier and he fell fast asleep.

The next day the store was full of people, but nobody paid any attention to Wobbly Bear. Then a little boy looked up at the shelf and cried, "Oh, what a lovely bear. Can I have that one, Daddy?"

Wobbly Bear's heart lifted as the little boy's daddy reached up to his shelf. But he picked up Brown Bear instead and handed him to the little boy. Wobbly Bear felt sadder than ever. Nobody wanted him. All of his new friends would get sold and leave the store, but he would be left on the shelf gathering dust. Poor old Wobbly Bear!

Now, Mr and Mrs Puppety had a little granddaughter called Jessie who loved to visit the store and play with the toys. All the toys loved her because she was gentle and kind. It so happened that the next time she came to visit it was her birthday, and her grandparents told her she could choose any toy she wanted as her present.

"I know she won't choose me," thought Wobbly Bear sadly. "Not with all these other beautiful toys to choose from."

But, to Wobbly's amazement, Jessie looked up and pointed at his shelf and said, "I'd like that wobbly bear please. No one else will have a bear quite like him."

Mr Puppety smiled and gave Wobbly to Jessie. She hugged and kissed him, and Wobbly felt so happy he almost cried. She took him home and put a smart red bow around his neck ready for her birthday party.

He felt very proud indeed.

Soon the other children arrived, each carrying their teddy bears under their arms.

Wobbly Bear could not believe his eyes when he saw the little boy with his friend Brown Bear!

"I'm having a teddy bears' picnic," Jessie explained to him, hugging him tight. All of the children and the bears had a wonderful time, especially Wobbly. He had found a lovely home, met his old friend and made lots of new ones.

"See, I told you not to worry," said Brown Bear.

"I know," said Wobbly. "And I never will again."

More Terrible Tongue Twisters

My dame hath a lame tame crane,
My dame hath a crane that is lame.
Pray, gentle Jane, let my dame's tame crane
Feed and come home again.

Six sick slick slim sycamore saplings.

She sifted thistles through her thistle-sifter.

Cows graze in groves on grass which grows in grooves in groves.

She sells sea shells by the sea shore.
The shells she sells are surely seashells.
So if she sells shells on the seashore,
I'm sure she sells seashore shells.

Sure the ship's shipshape, sir.

A big black bug bit a big black bear, made the big black bear bleed blood.

"Surely Sylvia swims!" shrieked Sammy, surprised.
"Someone should show Sylvia some strokes so she shall not sink."

Chop shops stock chops.

Can you imagine an imaginary menagerie manager imagining managing an imaginary menagerie?

Six sharp smart sharks.

One-One was a racehorse.
Two-Two was one, too.
When One-One won one race,
Two-Two won one, too.

I thought a thought.
But the thought I thought wasn't the thought I thought I thought.

Three twigs twined tightly.

Are our oars oak?

Six slippery snails, slid slowly seaward.

The Leith police dismisseth us,
   I'm thankful, sir, to say;
The Leith police dismisseth us,
   They thought we sought to stay.
The Leith police dismisseth us,
   We both sighed sighs apiece,
And the sigh that we sighed as we said goodbye
   Was the size of the Leith police.

The soldiers shouldered
shooters on their
shoulders.

Fred fed Ted bread,
and Ted fed Fred bread.

Freshly-fried flying fish.

A pleasant place to place a
plaice is a place where a
plaice is pleased to be placed.

Once upon a barren moor
   There dwelt a bear, also a boar.
The bear could not bear the boar.
   The boar thought the bear a bore.
At last the bear could bear no more
   Of that boar that bored him on the moor,
And so one morn he bored the boar –
   That boar will bore the bear no more.

Suddenly swerving, seven small swans
   Swam silently southward,
Seeing six swift sailboats
   Sailing sedately seaward.

Susan shineth shoes and socks;
   Socks and shoes shines Susan.
She ceased shining shoes and socks,
   For shoes and socks shock Susan.

On mules we find two legs behind
   And two we find before.
We stand behind before we find
   What those behind be for.

Horse Power

On the day of the Country Show, there was hustling and bustling on the farm. Mrs MacDonald had to feed the animals and collect the eggs by herself, because Old MacDonald was busy cleaning his tractor.

Every year, Old MacDonald gave rides on his tractor and trailer to the children. They loved it, but it was a lot of hard work for the farmer, with wheels to wash, and paint work to polish. Today, he also had ducks to shoo away when they began splashing about in the bubbles in his bucket!

But, at last, the tractor was spotlessly clean. Old MacDonald went into the farmhouse to put on his best boots.

"Here we go," said Doris the duck, as the farmer climbed into his tractor. "Cover your ears, little ones!"

But, when Old MacDonald turned the key, there was silence. The tractor simply would not start.

Old MacDonald tweaked the engine—and got his hands greasy. He stamped and stomped around—and got his best boots muddy. He muttered and moaned—and got rather red in the face. None of it did any good. The tractor didn't cough or splutter or show any sign of life.

"I hate to let the children down," groaned Old MacDonald. "But I can't pull the trailer if I don't have a tractor."

Now, Henry the cockerel is naughty and nosy, but sometimes he has good ideas. Henry jumped up on to Old George and Tilly's stable door and gave his loudest, "Cock-a-doodle-doo!"

Old MacDonald looked up in surprise, and then he gave a big smile.

"Goodness, gracious me!" he cried. "You're right, Henry—horse power! Now quick, jump out of the way. There's lots of work to be done!"

There were tails to untangle, coats to comb, and manes to thread with ribbons. There were harnesses to hitch and reins to clean and hang with gleaming brasses.

"It's just like the good old days," neighed Old George to Tilly.

There was no doubt who the stars of the Country Show were that year. Children lined up for ages, waiting to be pulled around by Old George and Tilly, who plodded proudly up and down with their coats shining and their heads held high.

At the end of the afternoon, Old MacDonald led the horses home and gave them a special supper of apples and oats.

"You know," he said with a sigh as he stroked their manes, "I miss the old days, too."

Old George and Tilly nodded their great heads, but it wasn't to show they agreed with him. They were asleep on their feet—they're not as young as they used to be, and it had been a very busy day!

A Spelling Lesson!

Wanda Witch went wandering through a very spooky wood. She loved to practise spooky spells, and the thought of doing anything good made her feel really ill.

She took great delight in turning a patch of beautiful bluebells into a pool of smelly, slimy goo. Then she gave a tree a creepy face that would frighten anyone who happened to be passing.

Creeping through the undergrowth, Wanda came upon a wizard, standing gazing into a pond. As quick as lightning, she waved her wand and the wizard fell straight into the water! Although the water wasn't very deep, it was very cold and full of horrible, slimy weeds.

The wizard leapt out in one huge jump, and was so angry with Wanda that he cast a spell as he landed next to her. His big red cloak wrapped itself around Wanda's body. Then it began to squeeze her really tight.

"Say sorry!" roared the wizard, "or you will stay like that!"

Wanda was shocked to have met someone who was even speedier and nastier than her! She apologised hastily to the wizard, and promised that from now on there would be no more nasty spells!

Witch's Brew

Winnie Witch was having a wonderful time! From her kitchen, deep inside a dark cave, came the sound of bubbling and singing as she stood stirring her huge cauldron. She was singing the spell for a magic monster as she threw the ingredients into the pot.

It had taken her days to collect the long list from her book of magic spells. Eye of lizard, toe of frog, tail of rat and bark of dog, sneeze of chicken, lick of weasel and smell of cat were all easy—but the cough of bat had been hard. Winnie had to chase a bat on her broomstick! It whizzed through the night sky so fast that Winnie thought she would fall off her broomstick. Eventually the bat must have choked on a fly. It coughed, spluttered, and slowed down. Winnie scooped up a cough and put it in her pocket before returning home for a rest!

The cauldron began to bubble furiously as Winnie stirred faster. Then… a monster's head began rising out of the pot.

"Ah!" sighed Winnie, "very pleased to meet you!"

"Mmm! Very pleased to *eat* you!" replied the monster!

Winnie went pale. Surely this wasn't right! She grabbed her wand and frantically shook it at the monster, whispering a spell. With a whoosh and a bang, the monster disappeared. Winnie won't be trying that spell again!

The Naughty Bears

One sunny summer's day, Ben and Fraser's parents told them to pack their things, as they were going to the beach.

"Yippee!" said Ben. "Can we take our teddies?"

"As long as you keep an eye on them this time," said Daddy. "We don't want to spend all afternoon looking everywhere for them if you lose them again!"

Ben and Fraser took their teddies everywhere they went, but they were always losing them, and then there was a great hunt to find them. But the truth was, that when no one was looking, the naughty little teddies would run away in search of excitement and adventure.

Today was no different. The family arrived at the beach and unpacked their things. Daddy sat reading a newspaper and Mommy took out a book. Soon Ben and Fraser were busy building sandcastles. When the naughty teddies saw that no one was looking, they jumped up and ran away giggling, all along the beach.

"Let's go exploring," said Billy, who was the oldest bear. "I can see a cave over there." He pointed to a dark hole in the rocks close to the water.

"It looks a bit dark and scary," said Bella.

"Don't be silly," said Billy. "You're a bear, aren't you? I thought that bears liked dark caves!"

The little bears clambered over the rocks and into the cave. It was very deep, and very dark. Just then, Bella spotted something gleaming on the floor. She picked it up and showed it to Billy.

"Gold!" said Billy, in excitement, taking the little coin from Bella. "This must be a smugglers' cave! Maybe the smugglers are still here. Let's take a look!"

"No!" said Bella. "They could be dangerous. Let's go back." She turned and ran back outside, where she saw to her horror that, while they had been exploring, the tide had come in, and cut the rocks off from the beach.

"Billy!" she called. "Come quickly, we're stranded!"

Meanwhile, Ben and Fraser had finished making sandcastles and found that their teddy bears were missing.

"Oh, no," groaned Daddy. "Not again!"

The family hunted high and low along the beach, but there was no sign of the bears to be found. "Maybe they've been washed out to sea," said Fraser, his voice trembling at the thought.

Back at the cave the naughty teddies could see their owners looking for them. They jumped up and down and waved their paws. "It's no use," said Bella, "they can't see us. We're too small."

"Don't worry," said Billy, trying to sound braver than he felt.

Just then, two men appeared from the other side of the rocks. The teddies froze —these must be the smugglers! They trembled in fear as the men picked them up, clambered over

the rocks, and tossed them into a little boat that had been hidden from view behind the rocks. The teddies clung together at the bottom of the boat as the men jumped in and began to row. Where were they taking them?

"Oh, Billy, I'm so frightened," whispered Bella. "Do you think they are going to hurt us?"

"No, Bella, I'm sure we'll be fine," answered Billy. But inside he didn't feel so sure. He was really very worried that they would never get home or see Ben and Fraser again.

Bella started to cry in little muffled whimpers, and big tears rolled down her cheeks. "If we ever get back home, I'm never going to run away again," she sobbed.

"There, there," comforted Billy, patting her gently.

After a while, the boat stopped and the men jumped out. They grabbed the bears and held them in the air high above their heads. One of the men called out in a loud voice, "Has anyone lost these bears?"

Everyone on the beach looked up, and Ben and Fraser raced over and grabbed their bears.

Daddy came running over to join them. He and the boys thanked the men for bringing the bears back. "We've been looking everywhere for them," said Ben and Fraser, grinning with relief.

"We found them up by that cave," said one of the men, pointing over to the cave. "You kids must have left them there."

"But the boys have been here building sandcastles all afternoon…" said Daddy, looking puzzled.

No one ever did find out how the naughty teddies got to the cave, or where the little coin in Billy's pocket came from. But from then on Daddy said they had to stay at home. The naughty teddies didn't really mind. They'd had enough adventures for the time being. And it gave them lots of time to play their favourite game—hide and seek!

No One Like You

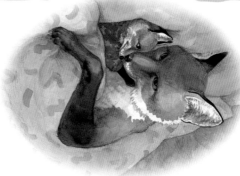

Ruff was hungry. A huge grumble rumbled round his tummy. He could hear Rufus clattering round in the kitchen. A delicious smell of freshly baked cakes sailed past his nose.

"Yummy," thought Ruff.

Ruff skipped into the kitchen—Rufus was washing up while the cakes cooled down.

"Would you like some help?" asked Ruff. "I could try one of those cakes for you."

"Oh, really!" said Rufus, smiling.

"No one makes cakes like you," said Ruff.

Ruff was bored. He twiddled his fingers, tapped his toes and twiddled his fingers again. He had no one to play with.

Later, Ruff tip-toed back into the living room—Rufus was reading.

"Would you like something better to read?" asked Ruff. "I could find you an exciting story."

"Oh, really!" said Rufus, smiling.

"No one tells a story like you," said Ruff.

Ruff was fed up. He was trying to make a model car. He fiddled and twiddled and fiddled, but he couldn't put it together.

Then he had an idea! Ruff galloped into the yard—Rufus was digging.

"Would you like something fun to do?" asked Ruff. "I could let you help me with my model car."

"Oh, really!" said Rufus, smiling.

"No one's as much fun as you," said Ruff.

It was bedtime! Rufus tucked Ruff into bed.

Ruff was feeling scared. He didn't like the shadows that flickered all round—it was very quiet. Then he had an idea! Ruff crept out of his bedroom and into Rufus' room.

Rufus was snoring loudly. It made Ruff giggle, which woke Rufus up.

"Would you like someone to cuddle?" asked Ruff. "I'm very good at cuddling."

"Oh, really!" said Rufus, smiling.

"No one cuddles like you," yawned Ruff, and he climbed into Rufus' bed.

"Oh, really!" said Rufus… "Well, no one loves you as much as I do, because there's no one like you."

Old Joe Brown

Old Joe Brown, he had a wife,
　　She was all of eight feet tall.
She slept with her head in the kitchen,
　　And her feet stuck out in the hall.

Poor Old Robinson Crusoe!

Poor old Robinson Crusoe!
　　Poor old Robinson Crusoe!
They made him a coat
　　Of an old nanny goat,
I wonder how they could do so!
　　With a ring a ting tang,
And a ring a ting tang,
　　Poor old Robinson Crusoe!

Old John Muddlecombe

Old John Muddlecombe lost his cap,
　　He couldn't find it anywhere, the poor old chap.
He walked down the High Street, and everybody said,
　　"Silly John Muddlecombe, you've got it on your head!"

Michael Finnegan

There was an old man called Michael Finnegan
　　He grew whiskers on his chinnegan
The wind came out and blew them in again
　　Poor old Michael Finnegan. Begin again...

Rub-a-dub Dub

Rub-a-dub dub,
　Three men in a tub,
And who do you think they be?
　The butcher, the baker,
The candle-stick maker,
　Turn them out knaves all three.

Tommy Thumb

Tommy Thumb, Tommy Thumb,
　Where are you?
Here I am, here I am,
　How do you do?

Peter Pointer, Peter Pointer,
　Where are you?
Here I am, here I am,
　How do you do?

Middle Man, Middle Man,
　Where are you?
Here I am, here I am,
　How do you do?

Ruby Ring, Ruby Ring,
　Where are you?
Here I am, here I am,
　How do you do?

Baby Small, Baby Small,
　Where are you?
Here I am, here I am,
　How do you do?

Fingers all, fingers all,
　Where are you?
Here we are, here we are,
　How do you do?

Solomon Grundy

Solomon Grundy,
　Born on Monday,
Christened on Tuesday,
　Married on Wednesday,
Sick on Thursday,
　Worse on Friday,
Died on Saturday,
　Buried on Sunday,
That was the end
　Of Solomon Grundy.

Jack Sprat

Jack Sprat could eat no fat,
　His wife could eat no lean,
And so between the two of them
　They licked the platter clean.

Old Everest

Everest was one of the biggest horses in the world. He was also one of the strongest. When he was young, and already twice as big as other horses, he pulled the heavy cart filled with peas or potatoes, cabbages or corn, and everything grown on the farm. He took the vegetables from the farm down to the market, and he brought things from the market back to the farm. He pulled the huge machine that cut the wheat to make flour. He pulled the big plow that dug the soil, so the farmer could plant the seed that grew into wheat that made the flour... that Everest took to market. He did everything!

Everest was the best... but that was ages ago.

"So why don't you do everything now?" asked Puff the Pig.

"The farmer thinks I'm too old," said Everest, sadly. "He is trying to be kind. He thinks I need a rest."

Jacob the Lamb said, "I bet you are still stronger than anything, Everest! Nothing is as strong as you!" The huge horse lowered his head.

"Well... I am not as strong as I was, little one," smiled Everest. "Anyway, farmers don't use horses any more. They use a tracto rinstead!"

The big old horse had lots of time to think about when he was young and still worked on the farm. He spent most of the time now in his favorite meadow nibbling grass, and, when he grew bored with that, chasing rabbits or chickens, or biting large chunks out of the hedge.

But if Parsnip the Sheep, Waddle the Goose, or Scratchitt the Cat were in his field, he would tell them his stories. Sometimes he told the same stories again without realising, but no one minded.

But Everest still thought about the tractor. It wasn't the tractor's fault. He just wanted to work.

"Why did the farmer buy the tractor?" Puff wanted to know. Everest lowered his huge head and sighed.

"He liked the color," said Everest.

Then one day the farmer said to Everest, "That tractor of mine! It won't start! I would ask you to help, Everest, but I suppose you are enjoying your rest." Everest shook his head from side to side.

"Even so," said the farmer, "I need to plow the field and the plow won't fit a horse, just the tractor! I don't know what to do."

Everest nudged the farmer gently over to the barn where the tractor was kept. His reins and harness were there too. The big horse picked up an old lead in his mouth and hooked it on the front of the tractor. Then, as easily as anything, he pulled out the tractor. Then he pulled the plow up behind the tractor.

"You mean you can pull both together?" said the farmer. Everest nodded his head up and down. The farmer was amazed! So the farmer hooked the plow to the tractor. Then he hooked the tractor to the horse. And Everest pulled the tractor and the tractor pulled the plow. Together they plowed the field in the fastest time ever.

Everest was still the biggest and the strongest... and now the happiest horse in the whole world.

Puppy's Paw

One sunny day, a small puppy sat in a grassy yard, watching Snowball and Snowdrop, his brother and sister, play. His coat was white with a few brown patches—and he had one brown paw. When he was born, his mommy said, "He looks like he's forgotten to put his other socks on! And that is how Socks got his name.

"Can I join in?" barked Socks.

"No, you can't!" Snowball yapped back.

"He looks like he's been having a mud bath, with those brown splodges," sneered Snowdrop. "Go and wash yourself properly, Socks."

"Maybe we should wash him," laughed Snowball. And the two puppies chased Socks towards the bird bath. Socks ran off as fast as he could and hid inside the shed—why didn't they like him? Was it because he didn't look like them? A big tear fell from his eye and trickled down his nose. Then, the two bouncy puppies appeared.

"Socks, where are you?" barked Snowdrop. Socks peeped out from behind the shed.

PUPPY'S PAW

"We're going to the wood for a walk, Socks," called Snowball. "Bye-bye!"

Socks couldn't help himself. He ran out on to the lawn. "Please can I come?" he begged.

"You're much too young to come with us," said Snowdrop. "And you know Mommy says that you're too young to go out without her."

"I'm not too young," whined Socks. "I've been out loads of times."

"Well, you can't walk with us," said Snowball. "You must walk behind us."

"Okay," yapped Socks, eagerly. So, the two pups scampered through the garden gate, with Socks following. Snowball and Snowdrop ran down the lane towards the wood—Socks trotted behind!

In a clearing, there were two paths to choose from. Snowball's nose began to twitch. He could smell something wonderful. "This way!" he yelped and the two older pups rushed off.

"Don't those two ever stop to look where they're going?" wondered Socks, as he lifted his brown paw and followed. Round a bend, the puppies found a huge clump of beautiful, pink flowers. Socks pushed his soft, black nose into them. "Atishoo!" he sneezed, as yellow pollen flew into the air.

Snowdrop was busy chasing a butterfly. It fluttered away down another path and Snowdrop followed. "Come on, Socks!" barked Snowball. "Keep up!" and he set off after his sister.

"We'll get lost if we're not careful," thought Socks.

The butterfly led the puppies deeper and deeper into the wood. Suddenly, it flew high into the air and disappeared. Snowdrop and Snowball stopped and looked around. There were trees everywhere and they all looked the same!

"How are we going to find our way home now?" wailed Snowball.

"Listen," woofed Snowdrop. "There's someone through those trees. Let's see if they know the way home."

"I know the way… " began Socks. But Snowball and Snowdrop weren't listening. They had already dashed off along the path.

"It's easy," thought Socks to himself and set off after the others.

Tap-tap! Tap-tap! A woodpecker was trying to find some insects in a tree. "Can you help us find our way home?" asked Snowball and Snowdrop. But the woodpecker flew off!

"What are we going to do now?" whined Snowdrop. "I want my mommy!"

"Help!" they howled. "Help!"

"But I know the way home!" said Socks.

Snowdrop and Snowball turned to their brother and stared. "What did you say?" they asked.

PUPPY'S PAW

"I said I know the way home," said Socks, again.

"How?" asked Snowball.

"It's easy," said Socks. "Every time we chose a path, we took the one on the side of my brown paw. To get home, we just turn round and take the path on the side of my white paw. Follow me and I'll show you."

So, back through the woods they went, with Socks in front. Each time they had to choose, Socks held up his brown paw, turned his head and took the other path. Back they scampered through the wood, past the pink flowers, down the lane, through the gate and into the yard, where their mommy was waiting for them.

"Where have you been?" she woofed, crossly. "I've been so worried."

"We got lost," said Snowball and Snowdrop. "It was all our fault."

"Socks was so clever," woofed Snowball. "We're so lucky to have him as a brother."

"I wish I had a brown paw like him," said Snowdrop. "Do you want to play ball, Socks?"

"Oh, yes please!" he woofed, flicking the ball across the lawn to his brother and sister. Sometimes it was good to be different!

Fishes Swim

Fishes swim in water clear,
   Birds fly up into the air,
Serpents creep along the ground,
   Boys and girls run round and round.

Cut Thistles

Cut thistles in May,
   They'll grow in a day;
Cut them in June,
   That is too soon;
Cut them in July,
   Then they will die.

Little Robin and Pussycat

Little Robin Redbreast jumped
   upon a wall,
Pussy cat jumped after him,
   and almost got a fall!
Little Robin chirped and sang,
   and what did pussy say?
Pussy cat said, "Mew" and
   Robin jumped away.

Little Robin Redbreast sat upon a tree,
   Up went pussy cat, and down
      went he!
Down came pussy, and away Robin ran;
   Says little Robin Redbreast,
    "Catch me if you can!"

Feathers

Cackle, cackle, Mother Goose,
   Have you any feathers loose?
Truly have I, pretty fellow,
   Half enough to fill a pillow.
Here are quills, take one or two,
   And down to make a bed for you.

You Shall be Queen

Lilies are white,
　　Rosemary's green,
When I am king,
　　You shall be queen.

Jemmy Dawson

Brave news is come to town,
　　Brave news is carried;
Brave news is come to town,
　　Jemmy Dawson's married.

First he got a porridge-pot,
　　Then he bought a ladle;
Then he got a wife and child,
　　And then he bought a cradle.

My Little Cow

I had a little cow,
　　Hey diddle, ho diddle!
I had a little cow,
　　and I drove it to the stall;
hey diddle, ho diddle!
　　and there's my song all.

The Coachman

Up at Piccadilly oh!
　　The coachman takes his stand,
And when he meets a pretty girl,
　　He takes her by the hand;
Whip away for ever oh!
　　Drive away so clever oh!
All the way to Bristol oh!
　　He drives her four-in-hand.

Jerry Hall

Jerry Hall,
　　He is so small,
A rat could eat him,
　　Hat and all.

Susie and the Mermaid

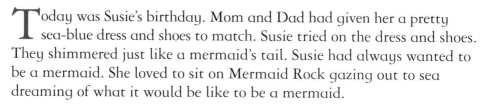

Today was Susie's birthday. Mom and Dad had given her a pretty sea-blue dress and shoes to match. Susie tried on the dress and shoes. They shimmered just like a mermaid's tail. Susie had always wanted to be a mermaid. She loved to sit on Mermaid Rock gazing out to sea dreaming of what it would be like to be a mermaid.

"I'll make a birthday wish," thought Susie, and closed her eyes. "I wish I could be a mermaid." When she opened her eyes, she was no longer wearing her birthday dress—she had a mermaid's tail! Susie couldn't believe her luck, her birthday wish had come true.

Then Susie heard someone crying. She looked around and saw someone sitting on the other side of Mermaid Rock wearing a blue dress just like her new birthday dress! "Why are you crying?" Susie asked the little girl.

"Because I've lost my tail," she replied. "You see, I'm a mermaid. But without my tail I can't go home!" Susie realised what had happened, her birthday wish must have made her swap places with the mermaid. Susie told the mermaid about her birthday wish.

"How can I change us back again?" asked Susie.

"If you can collect my tears from the sea, then you could wish again," said the mermaid.

Susie slipped into the sea. The water didn't feel a bit cold now that she was a mermaid. With her strong new

tail she swam quickly to the bottom of the sea.

Susie asked the sea creatures to help her search for the tears. Crabs and fish, lobsters and winkles peered into holes and lifted up stones, but it was no use. They couldn't find any tears. Susie didn't know what to do!

Then she heard, "One-two-three, one-two-three…" and from an underwater cave danced a large octopus wearing a long string of pearls! Its eight long arms whirled around as it danced and twirled.

"Hello, little mermaid!" said the octopus. "Can you help me?" asked Susie. "I'm looking for mermaid tears. But I don't know where to start."

"Ah! Well these pearls are just what you are looking for!" said the octopus. "That's what happens to mermaid tears you know—they turn into pearls! You can have them if you help me take them off!" laughed the octopus. "Oh, thank you so much!" cried Susie untangling the pearls.

"Farewell, little mermaid!" laughed the octopus as it danced away, singing, "One-two-three, one-two-three…"

Susie swam back to Mermaid Rock as quickly as she could with the pearls. Susie closed her eyes and wished again. Instantly, she was wearing her blue dress and the mermaid had her tail back.

"Thank you, Susie," said the mermaid. "I hope I'll see you again."

Susie waved goodbye as the mermaid slipped into the sea and swam away. Susie hurried home for her birthday tea. She glanced down at her new blue dress to make sure it was still clean. Down the front of the dress were sewn lots of tiny tear-shaped pearls!

The Birthday Party

Rosy was walking down the stairs, when the mail popped through the mail box and flopped on to the mat. One envelope had a picture of a rabbit and Rosy's name written in big writing on it. She picked it up and rushed into the kitchen. "Look, Mom!" cried Rosy, "a letter for me. Who do you think it's from?"

"I don't know," replied Mom. "Let's open it and find out."

Inside the envelope was an invitation to a party from Rosy's friend, Laura. "Wow! A party!" cried Rosy. "I can't wait!" she said and, with a little bit of help, answered "yes" to the invitation. But then, Rosy began to worry. "What am I going to buy Laura as a gift for her birthday?" she asked.

Mom had an idea. "Let's go into town tomorrow and look for something special." So, the next day, Rosy and Mom went to the toy store. "What does Laura like best?" said Mom.

"Rabbits," said Rosy. "Laura loves them."

"Come with me," smiled Mom. "I've seen just the thing."

Mom took Rosy to a corner of the toy store, where they found lots of fluffy toys. And there sat a cute little rabbit, with bright blue trousers and a tiny orange carrot. "Do you think Laura would like that rabbit?" asked Mom.

"She would love him," said Rosy. So, they bought the rabbit and some wrapping paper and went back home.

At home, Rosy wrapped the rabbit in the pretty paper. Then, she drew a card with a big rabbit on the front and wrote her name in red crayon inside it. "Mom," asked Rosy, "what will I do at the party?"

"Well, there will be lots of games to play," said Mom.

"I can't wait!" said Rosy.

At last, the afternoon of the party arrived. Rosy put on her pretty party dress. Mom gave her Laura's card and present. "Mom," asked Rosy, "what if I don't like the food?"

"Don't worry," said Mom. "At parties, there are always lots of tasty things to eat—I promise."

"I can't wait!" cried Rosy and skipped out of the door.

When Rosy arrived at the party, Laura opened the front door. There were lots of

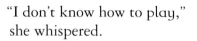

children standing behind her, but Rosy couldn't see anyone else that she knew. "Hello, Rosy," said Laura, giving her a big hug. Rosy gave Laura her birthday present. As Laura pulled off the paper, a huge smile spread across her face. "Oh, Rosy!" she cried. "He's perfect!"

Everyone wanted to hold the rabbit. Rosy felt better already. "Time for some games!" called Laura's mom. Rosy stood by the door and watched.

"I don't know how to play," she whispered.

"Just do what I do," said Laura and held her friend's hands. Rosy was soon having a wonderful time. Party games were great fun.

Just then, Laura's mom said, "It's time for the party food."

Rosy couldn't wait to see what there was to eat. She was feeling really hungry! "Wow!" gasped Rosy, when she saw the party food. All of her favorite things were there—sausages, pizza, cakes and strawberry jello! There were balloons, paper plates and cups, which all had rabbits on them.

Rosy sat next to Laura. "Wait till you see my cake," laughed her friend. At that moment, Laura's mom walked into the room. She was carrying a birthday cake —in the shape of a big rabbit! Laura blew out the candles and everyone sang "Happy birthday!" as loudly as they could.

THE BIRTHDAY PARTY

After tea, everyone played Pass the Parcel. Rosy really liked this game. It was very exciting, waiting for the music to stop and then watching, while someone tore the paper off the parcel. "I can't wait for my turn," thought Rosy. Suddenly, the music did stop, just as Rosy held the parcel. And this time, there was only one piece of paper left. She ripped it off—inside was a jigsaw puzzle.

It wasn't long before moms and dads came to take their children home. "Thanks for my rabbit," said Laura, to Rosy.

"And thanks for a great party," said Rosy. Then, Laura gave everyone a balloon and a badge—with a rabbit on it. On the way home, Mom asked Rosy if she'd had a good time.

"Oh, yes!" said Rosy. "The games were fun, Laura's other friends were great and the food was really yummy! Mom," said Rosy, "how long is it until my birthday?"

"About four weeks," said Mom. "Why?"

"Please can I have a party?" asked Rosy.

"I've got lots of friends to invite and I know just which games I want to play. And I'd really like a big dinosaur cake."

"I can't wait!" laughed Mom.

The Naughty Kitten

Ginger was a naughty little kitten. He didn't always mean to be naughty, but somehow things just turned out that way.

"You really should be more careful," warned Mommy. But Ginger was too busy getting into trouble to listen.

One day, Ginger was in a particularly playful mood. First, he tried to play tag with his smallest sister—and chased her right up an old apple tree. It took Daddy all morning to get her down.

Then, Ginger dropped cream all over the dog's tail. The dog whirled round and round as he tried to lick it off. He got so dizzy that he fell right over. That really made Ginger laugh until his sides hurt.

After that, Ginger thought it would be fun to play hide-and-seek with the mice—and frightened them so much that they refused to come out of their hole for the rest of the day.

Then, Ginger crept up behind the rabbit and shouted, "HI!" The poor rabbit was so surprised that he fell head-first into his breakfast. Ginger thought he looked ever so funny covered in lettuce leaves and carrots.

For his next trick, Ginger knocked over a wheelbarrow full of apples while he was trying to fly like a bird. He really couldn't help laughing when the apples knocked his little brother flying into the air.

And when one of the apples splashed into the garden pond, Ginger decided to go apple bobbing. How he laughed as the goldfish bumped into each other in their hurry to get out of his way.

Ginger laughed so much that, WHO-OO-AH! he began to lose his balance. He stopped laughing as he tried to stop himself falling into the pond. But, SPLASH! It was no good—he fell right in.

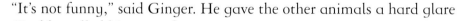

"Help! I can't swim," wailed Ginger, splashing wildly around. But he needn't have worried, the water only reached up to his knees.

"Yuck!" he moaned, squirting out a mouthful of water.

"Ha, ha, ha!" laughed the other kittens, who had come to see what the noise was about. And the dog and the rabbit soon joined in.

"You really should be more careful," said Mommy, trying not to smile.

"It's not funny," said Ginger. He gave the other animals a hard glare as Daddy pulled him out of the pond. But then he caught sight of his reflection in the water. He did look very funny. Soon he was laughing as loudly as the others.

After that, Ginger tried hard not to be quite so naughty. And do you know what? He even succeeded... some of the time!

Abou Ben Adhem

Abou Ben Adhem (may his tribe increase!)
Awoke one night from a deep dream of peace,
And saw, within the moonlight in his room,
Making it rich, and like a lily in bloom,
An angel writing in a book of gold:—
Exceeding peace had made Ben Adhem bold,

And to the presence in the room he said,
"What writest thou?"——The vision raided its head,
And with a look made of all sweet accord,
Answered, "The names of those who love the Lord."

"And is mine one?" said Abou. "Nay, not so,"
Replied the angel. Abou spoke more low,
But cheerily still; and said, "I pray thee then,
Write me as one that loves his fellow-men."

The angel wrote, and vanished.
The next night
It came again with a great
wakening light,

And showed the names whom
love of God had blessed,
And lo! Ben Adhem's name
led all the rest.

The Bells

Hear the sledges with the bells—
Silver bells!
What a world of merriment
their melody foretells!
How they tinkle, tinkle, tinkle,
In the icy air of night!
While the stars that oversprinkle
All the heavens, seem to twinkle
With a crystalline delight;
Keeping time, time, time,
In a sort of Runic rhyme,
To the tintinnabulation that so musically wells
From the bells, bells, bells, bells, bells, bells, bells—
From the jingling and the tinkling of the bells.

EDGAR ALLAN POE

Kubla Khan

In Xanadu did Kubla Khan
  A stately pleasure-dome decree;
Where Alph, the sacred river, ran
  Through caverns measureless to man
Down to a sunless sea.

    So twice five miles of fertile ground
      With walls and towers were girdled round;
    And here were gardens bright with sinuous rills
      Where blossomed many an incense-bearing tree;
    And here were forests ancient as the hills,
      Enfolding sunny spots of greenery.

Where Lies the Land

Where lies the land to which the ship would go?
  Far, far ahead, is all her seamen know.
And where the land she travels from? Away,
  Far, far behind, is all that they can say.
On sunny noons upon the deck's smooth face,
  Linked arm in arm, how pleasant here to pace;
Or, o'er the stern reclining, watch below
  The foaming wake far widening as we go.
On stormy nights when wild north-westers rave,
  How proud a thing to fight with wind and wave!
The dripping sailor on the reeling mast
  Exults to bear, and scorns to wish it past.

The Castle in the Clouds

There was once a family that lived in a little house, in a village at the bottom of a mountain. At the top of the mountain was a great, gray castle made of granite. The castle was always shrouded in clouds, so it was known as the castle in the clouds. From the village you could only just see the outline of its high walls and turrets. No one in the village ever went near the castle, for it looked such a gloomy and forbidding place.

Now in this family there were seven children. One by one they went out into the world to seek their fortune, and at last it was the youngest child's turn. His name was Sam. His only possession was a pet cat named Jess, and she was an excellent rat-catcher. Sam was most upset at the thought of leaving Jess behind when he went off to find work, but then he had an idea.

"I'll offer Jess's services at the castle in the clouds. They're bound to need a good ratter, and I'm sure I can find work there, too," he thought.

His parents were dismayed to discover that Sam wanted to find work at the castle, but they could not change his mind. So Sam set off for the castle with Jess at his side. It grew cold and misty as the road wound up the mountainside through thick pine forests. Rounding a bend they suddenly found themselves up against a massive, gray stone wall. They followed the curve of the wall until they came to the castle door.

Sam went up to the door and banged on it. The sound echoed spookily. "Who goes there?" said a voice.

Looking up, Sam saw that a window high in the wall had been opened and a face was eyeing him suspiciously.

"I... I... I wondered if you'd be interested in employing my cat as a rat-catcher," began Sam.

The window slammed shut, but a moment later the castle door opened. Stepping inside, Sam and Jess found themselves face-to-face with an old man. "Rat-catcher, did you say?" said the old man raising one eyebrow. "Very well, but she'd better do a good job or my master will punish us all!"

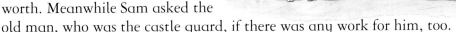

Sam sent Jess off to prove her worth. Meanwhile Sam asked the old man, who was the castle guard, if there was any work for him, too.

"You can help out in the kitchens, but it's hard work!" the guard said.

Sam was soon working very hard in the kitchens. He spent all day peeling vegetables, cleaning pans and scrubbing the floor.

By midnight he was exhausted. He was about to find a patch of straw to make his bed, when he noticed Jess wasn't around. He set off in search of her down dark passages, up winding staircases, but there was no sign of her. By now he was hopelessly lost but he suddenly saw Jess's green eyes shining like lanterns at the top of a rickety spiral staircase. "Here, Jess!" called Sam softly. But Jess stayed just where she was.

Jess was sitting outside a door and seemed to be listening to something on the other side. Sam put his ear to the door. He could hear the sound of sobbing. He knocked gently at the door. "Who is it?" said a girl's voice.

"I'm Sam, the kitchen boy. Can I come in?" said Sam.

"If only you could," sobbed the voice. "I'm Princess Rose. When my father died my uncle locked me in here so that he could steal the castle. Now I fear I shall never escape!"

Sam pushed and pushed at the door, but it was no use. "Don't worry," he said, "I'll get you out of here."

Sam knew exactly what to do. He had seen a pair of keys hanging on a nail in the rafters high above the guard's head. He had wondered why anyone should put keys out of the reach of any human hand. Now he thought he knew—but first he had to get the keys himself!

When Sam and Jess finally made their way back, they found the guard was fast asleep in his chair right underneath the keys! Jess leaped up on to the shelf behind his head, then she climbed until she reached the rafters. She took the keys in her mouth and carried them down. But, as she jumped from the shelf again, she knocked over a jug and sent it crashing to the floor. The guard woke with a start. "Who goes there?" he growled. He just caught sight of the tip of Jess's tail as she made a dash for the door.

"You go a different way," hissed Sam, running up the stairs to Rose's door, while the old man disappeared off after Jess. Sam put one of the keys in the lock. It fitted! He turned the key and opened the door. There stood the loveliest girl he had ever seen. The princess ran towards him, as he cried, "Quick! There's not a moment to lose." He grabbed her hand and led her out of the tower.

"Give me the keys," she said. She led him down to the castle cellars. At last they came to a tiny door. The princess put the second key in the lock and opened it. Inside was a cupboard, and inside that was a golden casket filled with jewels. "My own casket—stolen by my uncle," cried Rose.

Grabbing the casket, the pair ran to the stables and saddled a horse. Suddenly Jess appeared with the guard chasing him. With a mighty leap Jess landed on the back of the horse. "Off we go!" cried Sam.

And that was the last that any of them saw of the castle in the clouds. Sam married the princess and they all lived happily ever after.

Sports Day

The sun peeped over the higgledy-piggledy, messy alley. It was much too early to be awake—or was it? Lenny the kitten slowly opened his eyes and grinned—it was 'time-to-get-up' time.

"Get up, Sleepyhead!" he yelled to his twin sister, Lulu. "It's a great day for running and jumping." And he started to run round and round the garbage cans.

"Okay, Lenny," yawned Lulu, still half asleep, "I'm coming."

"I'll race you to the end of the alley," cried Lenny.

"But you always win," moaned Lulu.

"That's because you're a big, podgy pussy," laughed Lenny.

Lulu giggled. "Cheeky kitty!" she cried. "Bet you can't catch me!" And she ran down the alley as fast as she could.

"That was fun!" cried Lenny, as he finally caught up with his sister. "What about some jumping now?"

"Great idea," purred Lulu.

So, huffing and puffing, the little kittens piled up some boxes and put a pole across the gap.

Lenny leapt over it first. "Whee!" he cried. "I bet I can jump higher than you!"

Suddenly, Lulu spotted a tatty old ball. "I bet I can throw it further than you!" she cried.

"No, you can't," cried Lenny. He picked up the ball and threw his best throw ever— but it hit Uncle Bertie right on the head!

Scampering down the alley as fast as they could go, the two kittens quickly hid behind a heap of old potato sacks before Uncle Bertie could spot them!

"Pooh!" said Lulu. "These sacks are really very smelly!"

Suddenly, Lenny had an idea…

Sticking his feet into one of the old potato sacks, he pulled it up to his tummy and began hopping and jumping around!

"Hey, what about a sack race?" he giggled.

Lenny hopped and skipped. Lulu wiggled and giggled.

"I'm winning!" squealed Lulu. "I'm winning!"

"No, you're not!" cried Lenny. He jumped his best jump ever—and knocked a huge pile of boxes over Cousin Archie!

"Uh-oh!" groaned Lenny. "Trouble time!"

Uncle Bertie and Cousin Archie were not happy. They stomped off to find Hattie, the kittens' mother.

"Those kittens of yours are so naughty," they complained. "You've got to do something about them!"

Hattie sighed. Then, spying two pairs of tiny ears peeping out from behind a watering can, she tip-toed over. "Time-to-come-out-time!" she boomed.

"What have you two been up to?" Hattie asked Lenny and Lulu.

"Running and jumping, Mommy," whined Lenny.

"We didn't mean to hurt anyone," whispered Lulu. But Hattie wasn't cross. She knew her kittens were only playing.

"I've got an idea," she said. "Why don't we have a sports day? We can all join in—there'll be plenty of running and jumping for everyone!"

Archie and Bertie didn't want to play—wanted a cat nap!

"Okay," said Hattie. "We'll simply ask the dogs to join us instead."

So, later that day, Hattie explained her idea to the Alley Dogs, who all thought it sounded like great fun. And it wasn't long before Hattie had organised everyone and everything!

"We'll have lots of races," cried Lenny, excitedly, "running, skipping, leaping and jumping ones—perhaps a sack race!"

Suddenly, six pussy eyes peeped over the fence.

"Okay, everyone," cried Hattie. "Let's begin. Ready… steady… "

"Er, Hattie," asked Cousin Archie, popping out from behind the fence, "can I join in?"

"Us too?" cried Uncle Bertie and Auntie Lucy.

"Of course you can," laughed Hattie.

"Ready… steady… GO!"

Cousin Archie and Harvey raced up the alley and passed the winning line together. "Archie and Harvey are the winners!" cried Hattie. "Time for the sack race now!"

The dogs and cats all clambered into their sacks. But Lenny and Lulu began before Hattie could say "Go!"

"Hey!" cried Hattie. "Come back you two, that's cheating!" But it was too late. Everyone began leaping and jumping after the kittens.

"STOP!" shouted Hattie.

Lenny and Lulu stopped—but no one else did! They crashed into each other and fell in a big Alley cat and Dog pickle!

Luckily, no one was hurt, but now they were all tired.

"Well, that was the best sports day ever!" said Harvey.

Hattie looked at the higgledy-piggledy mess.

"You're right," she laughed. "But tomorrow we're going to play another game. It's called tidy-up the alley!"

Suddenly, lots of barking and meowing filled the air. "Oh, no!" they groaned, and then they all laughed.

The Princess of Hearts

Princess Ruby was given her name because she was born with ruby red lips the shape of a tiny heart. When she grew up she was very beautiful, with coal black hair down to her waist, green eyes and skin as pale as milk. She was a charming and friendly girl, but she insisted that everything she owned was heart-shaped! Her bed was heart-shaped, her table and chair were heart-shaped, even the sandwiches her maid brought her at teatime were cut into the shape of hearts!

As soon as she was old enough, the king and queen wanted Princess Ruby to find a husband. "There is a prince in the next kingdom who is looking for a wife," they told her. "He is brave and handsome and rich. Everything a princess could wish for."

But the foolish princess declared: "I will only marry this prince if he can change the stars in the sky to hearts!"

When Prince Gallant came to visit Princess Ruby she liked his kindly eyes and his pleasant smile. They spent the afternoon walking in the palace grounds, and talking about everything under the sun. But Prince Gallant could not promise to change the stars. As she watched the prince ride away, Princess Ruby suddenly wished she had not been so foolish!

Prince Gallant, too, was unhappy as he rode home. Suddenly, he heard a screeching sound. In the forest clearing, a dragon was attacking a peacock.

The prince took out his sword and chased the dragon away. The peacock's beautiful tail feathers were lying around him.

"Thank you for saving me," said the peacock. The prince was astonished to hear the peacock talk. "I have magical powers," explained the peacock. "But I am now very weak. The dragon has pulled out some of my magic feathers!"

The Prince set to work gathering up all the peacock's feathers. As soon as the feathers had been returned, the peacock gave a loud cry and spread his tail wide. The peacock's tail glowed.

"Before I go, I will grant you a single wish," he told the prince. Prince Gallant wished that the stars in the sky would take on the shape of hearts!

Later that night Princess Ruby was in her bedchamber. She was beginning to regret that she had refused to marry Prince Gallant.

She looked out of the window at the full moon and fields beyond the palace. Then she glanced at the stars—and couldn't believe her eyes!

Every single one was in the shape of a silver heart!

At that moment she saw Prince Gallant riding over the hill. He stopped his horse beneath Princess Ruby's window.

The prince again asked Princess Ruby if she would marry him. And of course she happily agreed!

They were married on a lovely summer's day. And, when Princess Ruby made her wedding vows, she promised never to ask for anything foolish, ever again!

Oranges and Lemons

Oranges and lemons,
  Say the bells of St Clements.
I owe you five farthings,
  Say the bells of St Martins.
When will you pay me?
  Say the bells of Old Bailey.
When I grow rich,
  Say the bells of Shoreditch.

London Bridge is Falling Down

London bridge is falling down,
  Falling down, falling down,
London bridge is falling down,
  My fair lady.

Frère Jacques

Frère Jacques, Frère Jacques,
  Dormez-vous, dormez-vous?
Sonnez les matines,
  Sonnez les matines,
Ding, dang, dong,
  Ding, dang, dong.

The Miller of Dee

There was a jolly miller
  Lived on the river Dee:
He worked and sang from morn till night,
  No lark so blithe as he;
And this the burden of his song
  For ever used to be—
I jump mejerrime jee!
  I care for nobody—no! not I,
Since nobody cares for me.

Ding Dong Bell

Ding, dong, bell,
  Pussy's in the well!
Who put her in?
  Little Tommy Green.
Who pulled her out?
  Little Johnny Stout.
What a naughty boy was that
  To try to drown poor pussy cat,
Who never did any harm,
  But killed the mice in his
  father's barn.

The Bells of London

Gay go up and gay go down,
  To ring the bells of London town.
Halfpence and farthings,
  Say the bells of St Martin's.
Pancakes and fritters,
  Say the bells of St Peter's.
Two sticks and an apple,
  Say the bells of Whitechapel.

Little Cottage in the Wood

Little cottage in the wood,
  Little old man by the window stood,
Saw a rabbit running by,
  Knocking at the door.
"Help me! Help me! Help me!" he said,
  "Before the huntsman shoots me dead."
"Come little rabbit, come inside,
  Safe with me abide."

Have You Seen the Muffin Man?

Have you seen the muffin man,
  the muffin man, the muffin man,
Have you seen the muffin man
  that lives in Drury Lane O?

Yes, I've seen the muffin man,
  the muffin man, the muffin man;
Yes, I've seen the muffin man who
  lives in Drury Lane O.

The Smart Bear and the Foolish Bear

It was the start of winter. The first snow had fallen, and the lake had begun to freeze. It was nearly time for all the bears to start their winter sleep. But there was one foolish bear who wasn't ready to sleep yet. "I'll just catch one more fish," he told himself, "to keep me going through winter." And, although he knew it was dangerous, he crept out onto the icy lake.

He lay down on his tummy, and broke a hole in the ice. He could see lots of fish swimming in the water below. He dipped his paw into the hole, and scooped out a fish in a flash! But the foolish little bear leapt up, shouting, "I caught one!" With a great crack, the ice gave way beneath him, and he fell into the freezing water!

Luckily a smart little bear cub heard his cries, and rushed to help. He found a fallen log and pushed it over the ice. The foolish bear grabbed it, and pulled himself to safety, still holding the fish.

"How can I thank you?" he asked.

"That fish would do nicely," said the smart little bear, and he strolled away to start his winter's sleep.

Rusty's
Big Day

Long ago there lived a poor farmer called Fred, who had a horse called Rusty. Once Rusty had been a good, strong horse. He had willingly pulled the plow and taken his master into town to sell his vegetables. Now he was too old to work on the farm, but the farmer couldn't bear to think of getting rid of him because he was so sweet-natured. "It would be like turning away one of my own family," Fred used to say. Rusty spent his days grazing in the corner of the field. He was quite content, but he felt sad that he was no longer able to help the poor farmer earn his living.

One day, Fred decided to go to town to sell a few vegetables. He harnessed Beauty, the young mare, to the wagon and off they went.

Beauty shook her fine mane and tossed a glance at Rusty as if to say, "Look who's queen of the farmyard!"

While Fred was in the town, his eye was caught by a notice pinned to a tree. It said:

Horse Parade at 2 pm today
The winner will pull the king's carriage to the Grand Banquet tonight

"There's not a moment to lose, my girl!" said Fred. "We must get you ready for the parade." And he turned the wagon around. "Giddy-up, Beauty!" he called, and she trotted all the way back to the farm.

Fred set to work to make Beauty look more lovely than she had ever done before. He scrubbed her hoofs and brushed her coat until it shone. Then he plaited her mane and tied it with a bright red ribbon. Rusty watched from the field. "How fine she looks," he thought, wistfully. "She's sure to win." He felt a bit sad that he was too old to take part in the parade, so he found a patch of the sweetest grass to graze on, to console himself.

All at once, he heard Fred approach. "Come on, old boy," he said, "you can come, too. It'll be fun for you to watch the parade, won't it?"

Rusty was thrilled. It was a long time since the master had last taken him into town.

Soon the three of them set off back into town, with Fred riding on Beauty's back and Rusty walking by their side. When they reached the parade ground, there were already a lot of people and horses there. There were horses of every shape and size!

The parade began. The king and members of the royal court entered the parade ground and took their places. Then the king announced three contests. First there would be a race from one end of the parade ground to the other. Then there would be a contest of strength. Each horse would have to try to pull a heavy carriage. Lastly, there would be a trotting competition. Each horse would have to carry a rider around the parade ground.

Rusty tried his best, but he couldn't compete with the younger horses in the race and the contest of strength. All the other horses stared at him. "What's an old horse like you doing taking part in a contest like this?" one of them asked disdainfully. "You shouldn't have been allowed to compete at your age!" taunted another.

Then came the trotting competition. "I shall ride each horse in turn," declared the king. He climbed up on to the first horse, but it bolted and left the king hanging by the stirrups. The next horse threw the king right up in the air! The next horse was so nervous that his teeth chattered. Then it was Beauty's turn. She carried the king magnificently, until she stumbled at the end. At last it was Rusty's turn. Rusty carried the king quite slowly and steadily, making sure he picked his feet up carefully, so that his royal highness would not be jolted. "Thank you for a most pleasant ride," said the king dismounting. There was a hush as the horses and their owners awaited the result of the contest. "I have decided," announced the king, "that Rusty is the winner. Not only did he give me a most comfortable ride, but he accepted his other defeats with dignity. Speed and strength are not everything, you know."

Rusty and Fred were overjoyed, and even Beauty offered her congratulations. "Although I probably would have won if I hadn't stumbled," she muttered.

So Rusty proudly pulled the king's carriage that evening, and he made such a good job of it that the king asked him if he would do it again the following year. Then the king asked Fred if his daughter could ride Beauty from time to time. He even gave Fred a bag of gold to pay for the horses' upkeep. So the three of them were happy as they never had been before as they returned home to the farm that night.

One Man Went To Mow

One man went to mow, went to mow a meadow,
One man and his dog, Spot,
Went to mow a meadow.

Two men went to mow, went to mow a meadow,
Two men, one man and his dog, Spot,
Went to mow a meadow.

Three men went to mow, went to mow a meadow,
Three men, two men, one man and his dog, Spot
Went to mow a meadow.

Four men went to mow, went to mow a meadow,
Four men, three men, two men, one man and his
dog, Spot,
Went to mow a meadow.

Hey de Ho

Hey de, hey de ho,
   The great big elephant
Is so slow.
   Hey de, hey de ho,
The elephant is so slow.

He swings his tail
   From side to side,
As he takes the children
   For a ride.

Hey de, hey de ho,
   The elephant is so slow.

Tom, He Was a Piper's Son

Tom, he was a piper's son,
   He learnt to play when he was young,
And all the tune that he could play,
   Was, "Over the hills and far away."

Over the hills and a great way off,
   The wind shall blow my topknot off.

Little Miss Muffet

Little Miss Muffet
  Sat on a tuffet,
Eating her curds and whey;
  There came a big spider,
Who sat down beside her,
  And frightened Miss Muffet away.

Little Bo-Peep

Little Bo-peep has lost her sheep,
  And can't tell where to find them;
Leave them alone, and they'll come home,
  And bring their tails behind them.

Little Bo-peep fell fast asleep,
  And dreamt she heard them bleating;
But when she awoke, she found it a joke,
  For they were still a-fleeting.

Then up she took her little crook,
  Determined for to find them;
She found them indeed, but it made her heart bleed,
  For they'd left all their tails behind'em.

The Farmer's in his Den

The farmer's in his den,
  The farmer's in his den,
E I E I
  The farmer's in his den.

The farmer wants a wife,
  The farmer wants a wife,
E I E I
  The farmer wants a wife.

The wife wants a child,
  The wife wants a child,
E I E I
  The wife wants a child.

The child wants a nurse,
  The child wants a nurse,
E I E I
  The child wants a nurse.

The nurse wants a dog,
  The nurse wants a dog,
E I E I
  The nurse wants a dog.

We all pat the dog,
  We all pat the dog,
E I E I
  We all pat the dog.

Milly the Greedy Puppy

Milly the Labrador puppy just loved eating. She wasn't fussy about what she ate, and didn't really mind whom it belonged to.

"You'll get fat," warned Tom, the farm cat. But Milly was too busy chewing a tasty fishbone to take any notice.

One day, Milly was in a particularly greedy mood. Before breakfast she sneaked into the kitchen and ate Tom's biscuits. After a big breakfast of fresh sardines and milk, she took a short break before nibbling her way through the horse's oats. The horse didn't seem to mind.

Then Milly had a quick nap. She felt quite hungry when she awoke, so she ate all the tastiest titbits from the pigs' trough. But she made sure she left plenty of room for lunch.

After a light lunch, Milly couldn't help feeling just a bit hungry—so she wolfed down Farmer Jones's meat pie. He'd left it on the window ledge so he obviously didn't want it.

After that, Milly knocked over the trash can and rifled through the kitchen waste. It was full of the yummiest leftovers.

There was just enough time for another nap before nipping into the milking shed for milking time. Milly always enjoyed lapping up the odd bucketful of fresh milk when Farmer Jones wasn't looking.

MILLY THE GREEDY PUPPY

Dinner was Milly's favorite meal of the day. It was amazing how fast she could eat a huge bowl of meat and biscuits.

Before going to bed, Milly walked around the yard cleaning up the scraps the hens had left behind. Wasn't she a helpful puppy!

Just as Milly was chewing a particularly tasty bit of bread, she saw something black out of the corner of her eye. It was Tom the farm cat, out for his evening stroll. If there was one thing Milly liked doing best of all, it was eating Tom's dinner when he wasn't looking.

Milly raced across the yard, around the barn and through the cat flap.

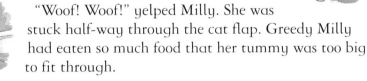

"Woof! Woof!" yelped Milly. She was stuck half-way through the cat flap. Greedy Milly had eaten so much food that her tummy was too big to fit through.

"Ha! Ha!" laughed the farm animals, who thought it served Milly right for eating all their food.

"Oh, dear!" smiled Tom when he came back to see what all the noise was about. He caught hold of Milly's legs and tried pulling her out. Then he tried pushing her out. But it was no good—she was stuck.

All the farm animals joined in. They pulled and pulled, until, POP! Out flew Milly.

Poor Milly felt so silly that she never ate anyone else's food again—unless they offered, that is!

Gym Giraffe

Jeremy Giraffe loved going out with his dad to gather the juicy green leaves for their dinner.

"This is where the most delicious leaves are," said Dad, reaching w-a-a-a-y up to a very high branch. "Remember the tallest trees have the tastiest leaves, and the tiny top leaves are the tenderest!"

One morning, Jeremy decided it was time to gather leaves on his own. "The tallest trees have the tastiest leaves," he whispered to himself, "and the tiny top leaves are the tenderest."

Jeremy stopped at a very tall tree and looked up. There at the top were some tiny, tender, tasty-looking leaves. Str - e - e - e - e - etching his neck just as he had seen his dad do, Jeremy reached as high as he could. It wasn't very high! "Oh, no," he thought. "How will I reach the tiny, tasty top leaves if my neck won't stretch?"

So Jeremy went back home with his neck hanging down in despair.

"Why, Jeremy, what's wrong?" asked his mom. When Jeremy told her, she gave his neck a nuzzle. "Your neck's still growing," she assured him. "Eat your greens and get lots of sleep, and you'll soon be able to reach the tastiest, tenderest leaves on the tallest trees in the jungle!"

That afternoon, Jeremy went out to try again. Portia Parrot saw Jeremy struggling to reach the top of the tree. Trying to be helpful, she swooped down and plucked a few of the tenderest leaves for him.

When Portia gave Jeremy the leaves, his spots went pale with shame and embarrassment.

"I should be able to get those myself," he wailed. "Why won't my neck stretch?"

"Oh, Jeremy," said Portia, "your neck is just fine! Keep eating your greens and getting lots of sleep, and it will grow!"

"But I can't wait," Jeremy insisted. "Isn't there anything I can do to stretch my neck now?"

"Perhaps there is," said Portia, thoughtfully. "Follow me!"

Portia led Jeremy through the jungle to a clearing. Jeremy's eyes widened with wonder at what he saw. There was so much going on! Seymour Snake was wrapping himself round a fallen tree trunk. "Hello, Jeremy," he hissed. "Jussssst doing my sssssslithering exercisesssss!"

Emma, Ellen and Eric Elephant were hoisting logs. "Hi, Jeremy," they called. "This is our trunk-strengthening workout!"

In the river, Claudia Crocodile was breaking thick branches in half. "Just limbering up my jaw muscles," she snapped.

Leonard Lion was taking his cubs, Louis and Lisa, through their pouncing paces. "Welcome to the Jungle Gym!" he called.

A few minutes later, Grandpa Gorilla and Leonard Lion came to greet Jeremy.

"What can we do for you?" they asked.

"Can you help me stretch my neck?" asked Jeremy. "I want to be able to reach the tasty, tiny, tender leaves."

"You're still growing," said Leonard Lion. "You just have to eat your greens and get lots of sleep."

Jeremy's face fell, until Grandpa Gorilla said, "But we will help things along with some special neck-stretching exercises. Come with us!"

Grandpa got Jeremy started right away.

"S-t-r-e-t-c-h to the left! S-t-r-e-t-c-h to the right!" Grandpa Gorilla shouted. "Chin lifts next," said Leonard Lion.

Jeremy s-t-r-e-e-e-t-c-h-e-d his neck to reach the branch.

"Come on, you can do it!" Portia said, cheering him on. Grandpa Gorilla told Jeremy to lie down. Then he called Seymour Snake. "Start slithering!" he said.

"Aaaaakkkk!" gasped Jeremy, as Seymour wrapped himself round his neck. "Not so tight," said Grandpa.

"That's better!" said Jeremy, as Seymour slithered along, pu-u-u-l-l-ing his neck muscles. All the exercise made Jeremy hungry.

At supper, he had three BIG helpings of greens. He was tired, too, so he went to bed early and slept soundly.

Jeremy loved the Jungle Gym and couldn't wait to go back. After his workout each day, Jeremy ate a good supper.

"Exercising makes me soooo hungry..." he said, "...and soooo tired," he yawned, as he fell asleep.

GYM GIRAFFE

The next time Jeremy and his dad went out leaf-gathering together, Jeremy spotted some sweet-looking leaves right at the top of a tall tree.

"I'm going to get those," he said.

"They're so high up!" said Dad.

Jeremy didn't hear him. He was too busy stretching… and stretching… and stretching… until he stretched right up to the very top branch!

"I've done it, Dad!" he cried happily. "The exercises worked!"

"I don't think it matters," said his mom. "What matters is that you have a fine, strong, long neck that any giraffe would be proud of!"

"And I am!" said Jeremy, taking another mouthful of tasty, tender leaves. He chewed the leaves extra thoroughly— because he knew they had a very long way to go!

The Fieldmouse

Where the acorn tumbles down,
　There the ash tree sheds its berry,
With your fur so soft and brown,
　With your eye so round and merry,
Scarcely moving the long grass,
　Fieldmouse, I can see you pass.

Little thing, in what dark den,
　Lie you all the winter sleeping?
Till warm weather comes again,
　Then once more I see you peeping
Round about the tall tree roots,
　Nibbling at their fallen fruits.

Fieldmouse, fieldmouse, do not go,
　Where the farmer stacks his treasure,
Find the nut that falls below,
　Eat the acorn at your pleasure,
But you must not steal the grain
　He has stacked with so much pain.

Make your hole where mosses spring,
　Underneath the tall oak's shadow,
Pretty, quiet, harmless thing,
　Play about the sunny meadow.
Keep away from corn and house,
　None will harm you, little mouse.

CECIL FRANCES ALEXANDER

The Camel's Complaint

Canary-birds feed on sugar and seed,
　Parrots have crackers to crunch;
And as for the poodles, they tell me the noodles
　Have chicken and cream for their lunch.
　　But there's never a question
　　About *my* digestion—
　　　Anything does for me.

Cats, you're aware, can repose in a chair,
　Chickens can roost upon rails;
Puppies are able to sleep in a stable,
　And oysters can slumber in pails.
　　But no one supposes
　　A poor camel dozes—
　　　Any place does for me.

The Tyger

Tyger! Tyger! burning bright
　In the forests of the night,
What immortal hand or eye
　Could frame thy fearful symmetry?

In what distant deeps or skies
　Burnt the fire of thine eyes?
On what wings dare he aspire?
　What the hand dare seize the fire?

And what shoulder, and what art,
　Could twist the sinews of thy heart?
And, when thy heart began to beat,
　What dread hand? and what dread feet?

What the hammer? what the chain?
　In what furnace was thy brain?
What the anvil, what dread grasp
　Dare its deadly terrors clasp?

When the stars threw down their spears,
　And water'd heaven with their tears,
Did he smile his work to see?
　Did he who made the Lamb make thee?

Tyger! Tyger! burning bright
　In the forests of the night,
What immortal hand or eye,
　Dare frame thy fearful symmetry?

WILLIAM BLAKE

Wynken, Blynken, and Nod

Wynken, Blynken,
　and Nod one night
Sailed off in a
　wooden shoe—
Sailed on a river
　of crystal light,
Into a sea of dew.

"Where are you going,
　and what do you wish?"
The old moon asked
　the three.
"We have come to fish
　for the herring fish
That live in this beautiful sea.

Jimbo Comes Home

Jimbo the circus elephant was snoring away in his cage one night when he heard a strange noise. At first he thought it was part of his dream. In his dream he was walking across a hot, dusty plain while in the distance there was the sound of thunder.

All at once Jimbo was wide awake. He realised that he was in his cage after all and that what he thought was the sound of thunder was the noise of his cage on the move. Now this worried him, because the circus never moved at night. He rose to his feet and looked around. He could see men pulling on the tow bar at the front of the cage. These were strangers—it certainly wasn't Carlos his trainer! Jimbo started to bellow, "Help! Stop thief!" But it was too late. His cage was already rumbling out of the circus ground and down the road.

Eventually, the cage passed through a gate marked "Zipper's Circus" and Jimbo knew what had happened. He had been stolen by the Zipper family, his own circus family's greatest rivals! Jimbo was furious. How had the

thieves got away with it? Surely someone at Ronaldo's Circus must have heard them stealing him? But Jimbo waited in vain to be rescued.

The next morning, the thieves opened up Jimbo's cage and tried to coax him out, but he stayed put. In the end, after much struggling, they managed to pull him out. Once he was out of his cage, he took the biggest drink of water he could from a bucket and soaked his new keeper! He refused to co-operate, kicked over his food, and when he appeared in the circus that night he made sure he got all the tricks wrong.

"Don't worry," said Mr Zipper to Jimbo's new trainer, "he'll just take a little while to settle down. Soon he'll forget that he was once part of Ronaldo's Circus." But Jimbo didn't forget for, as you know, an elephant never forgets.

One night, a mouse passed by his cage. "Hello," called Jimbo mournfully, for by now he was feeling very lonely, and no one had cleaned out his cage for days.

"Hello!" said the mouse. "You don't look very happy. What's the matter?" Jimbo explained how he had been stolen and wanted to escape back to his own circus. The mouse listened and then said, "I'll try to help."

So saying, he scampered off and soon he was back with a bunch of keys. Jimbo was astonished. "Easy!" said the mouse. "The keeper was asleep, so I helped myself."

Jimbo took the keys in his trunk and unlocked the door to the cage. He was free! "Thank you!" he called to the mouse, who was already scurrying away.

Jimbo's first thought was to get back to his own circus as fast as possible. However, he wanted to teach those thieves a lesson. He could hear them snoring in their caravan. He tiptoed up, as quietly as an elephant can tiptoe, and slid into the horse's harness at the front.

"Hey, what do you think you're doing?" neighed one of the horses, but Jimbo was already hauling the robbers' caravan out of the gate and down the road.

So gently did he pull the caravan that the thieves never once woke up. Eventually they reached Ronaldo's Circus. Mr Ronaldo was dumbstruck to see Jimbo pulling a caravan just like a horse! Mr Ronaldo walked over to the caravan and was astonished to see the robbers still fast asleep. He raced to the telephone and called the police, and it wasn't until they

heard the police siren that the robbers woke up. By then it was too late. As they emerged from the caravan scratching and shaking their heads they were arrested on the spot and taken off to jail. "There are a few questions we would like to ask Mr Zipper regarding the theft of some other circus animals, too," said one of the police officers.

Mr Ronaldo, and Jimbo's keeper Carlos, were both delighted to see Jimbo back home again. And Jimbo was just as delighted to be back home. Then Mr Ronaldo and Carlos started whispering to each other and began walking away looking secretive. "We'll be back soon, we promise," they said to Jimbo. When they returned, they were pushing Jimbo's old cage. It had been freshly painted, there was clean, sweet-smelling straw inside, but best of all there was no lock on the door! "Now you can come and go as you please," said Carlos.

And Jimbo trumpeted long and loud with his trunk held high, which Carlos knew was his way of saying, "THANK YOU!"

The Dotty Professor

Professor Von Bean was very excited. He had finished building his machine and it was ready to use. It was the most complicated contraption he had ever built and he was very proud of it.

The professor called his assistant to come to watch him start the machine. The wheels were green and brown, and there were levers on either side. The side panels were striped red and white, and there was a big chimney on the top for the smoke to escape. There was a closet on the side which, the professor explained, was to hang a wet coat. There was a shelf on the back for a box of plants.

While Professor Von Bean was getting more and more excited, his assistant looked very worried and puzzled.

"But what does it *do*?" he asked, timidly.

The professor scratched his head and thought.

"Oh dear, oh dear!" he sighed. "What a fool I have been! Why I didn't think of that? It does absolutely nothing useful at all!"

My Funny Family

I think that there is definitely something very strange about my family, in fact they are all very funny!

My auntie May has got a brain like a sieve, she forgets where things live. She puts a chop in the teapot and carrots in the mugs!

My uncle Fred has ears like cauliflowers, he can hear an ant whistling from a mile away, butterflies beating their wings and woodlice snoring!

My cousin Bob has eyes like a hawk, he can see from London to New York and unknown planets orbiting in space!

My brother Tom has spiders and bugs up his sleeve, which he loves to wave under my nose so that I scream.

My dog Jasper will eat anything, but especially loves hamburgers, cakes and buttered toast.

Luckily I am not so strange, I just like to dance all day!

Rapunzel

Once upon a time there lived a couple who, after many years, found they were expecting a baby.

Their tiny cottage stood next to a river. Across the river was a beautiful garden full of glorious flowers and tasty-looking vegetables. One day, the woman looked across the river and saw a vegetable called rampion growing in the garden. It looked delicious, and she longed to taste it. She begged her husband to get some.

The garden belonged to an evil witch, and he refused. But his wife would eat nothing else, and grew thin and pale. At last he agreed.

That night, the man crossed the river, entered the witch's garden and picked handfuls of rampion. Suddenly, the evil witch appeared. "How dare you steal from me!" she roared.

"F-Forgive me," the man stammered. "My wife is expecting a baby and longed for some of this vegetable. If she doesn't have it, I'm afraid she will die."

"Very well," said the witch, "take all you want. But you must give me something in return. When your baby is born, I must have it."

Terrified, the man agreed and fled.

The wife was overjoyed and made a salad with the rampion. She ate it hungrily.

After that, the man went to the witch's garden every day. He brought home baskets full of rampion for his wife, and she grew strong and healthy. A few months later she gave birth to a beautiful baby girl.

The man had forgotten all about his promise to the witch, but when the baby was just a day old, she burst in and took her away. The baby's parents were heartbroken and never saw her or the witch again.

The witch called the baby Rapunzel. She took her to a cottage deep in a forest, and took good care of her.

On Rapunzel's twelfth birthday, the witch imprisoned her in a forbidding high tower, with no doors and just one small window at the very top.

Every day the witch came and stood at the bottom of the tower, and called:
"Rapunzel, Rapunzel!
Let down your long hair!"

Rapunzel would let down her long, golden hair, and the witch would begin to climb up.

Rapunzel spent many lonely years in her tower. To pass the time, she often sat by the window and sang.

One day, a prince rode through the forest. Enchanted by the sound of Rapunzel's sweet voice, the young prince followed it until he came to the doorless tower.

Just then the witch arrived. The prince quickly hid as she called:
"Rapunzel, Rapunzel!
Let down your long hair!"

The witch began to climb the hair, and the prince knew that this was the way he would be able to meet the owner of the beautiful voice.

After the witch had gone, the prince stood beneath the tower and called in a voice like the witch's:

"Rapunzel, Rapunzel!
Let down your long hair!"

When Rapunzel's golden hair came tumbling down, he climbed up to the window.

Rapunzel was frightened when she saw the prince. But he was gentle and kind, and she quickly lost her fear.

The prince came to see Rapunzel often, and they soon fell in love. He asked her to marry him—but how would Rapunzel leave the tower?

Rapunzel had an idea. "Each time you visit," she told the prince, "bring me a ball of strong silk.

I will plait it into a long, long ladder. When it is finished I will climb down and run away to marry you."

The prince did as Rapunzel asked, and soon the ladder was ready.

But, on the very day she was to run away, something terrible happened. When the witch climbed through the window, Rapunzel absent-mindedly asked, "Why do you pull so hard at my hair? The prince is not so rough." Suddenly, Rapunzel realised what she had said.

The witch flew into a raging fury. "You ungrateful little wretch!" she screamed. "I have protected you from the world, and you have betrayed me. Now you must be punished!"

"I'm sorry," Rapunzel sobbed, as she fell to her knees. "I didn't mean to make you cross."

The witch grabbed a pair of scissors and—snip-snap-snip-snap—cut off Rapunzel's long golden hair.

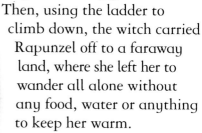

Then, using the ladder to climb down, the witch carried Rapunzel off to a faraway land, where she left her to wander all alone without any food, water or anything to keep her warm.

That evening, when the prince called, the witch let down Rapunzel's hair. The prince climbed up quickly, and couldn't believe his eyes!

"The bird has flown, my pretty!" the witch cackled evilly. "You will never see Rapunzel again!"

Overcome with grief, the sad

prince threw himself from the tower. His fall was broken by some brambles, but they also scratched and blinded him.

The prince stumbled away and wandered the land for a year, living on berries and rain water.

Then one day the prince heard a beautiful sound—the sweet voice of Rapunzel! He called her name and she ran into his arms, weeping tears of joy. The tears fell onto the prince's wounded eyes and suddenly he could see again.

The prince took his Rapunzel home to his castle, where they were married and lived happily ever after.

The Soccer Fairy

Georgina loved to play soccer. But there was just one problem. "I'm fed up with these silly wings," she said, wiggling her shoulders. "They just get in the way."

"Flying is brilliant, and anyway soccer is a game for elves, not fairies!" said Sparkle.

"In that case, I don't want to be a fairy!" said Georgina, and stamped off. "She'll change her mind," said the wise fairy, "just wait and see."

But Georgina wouldn't change her mind. She pulled on her soccer shoes and went to play with the elves.

The soccer game was very rough. The ball bounced around the field and, quite often, off the field! Sometimes it went up into the trees. Two birds who were trying to build their nest got very fed up.

Georgina flew up to get it. "Perhaps my wings can be useful after all," she thought. She looked round quickly, hoping no one had seen her.

But Barry, the elf, had and he couldn't wait to tell the fairies. "Ah," nodded the wise fairy. "I knew she would use her wings sooner or later."

The next time Georgina played soccer, the game was rougher than ever. One elf kicked the ball so hard it flew into the tree and hit the birds' nest. This time there was an egg in it! The egg began to topple, but none of the elves noticed; they were far too busy arguing with the referee.

Georgina flew up and, just in time, caught the egg before it hit the ground. Then she flew up to the nest.

"Thank you," said the mommy bird, tucking the egg back under her. "But please, be more careful when you play soccer!"

Next time she played soccer, Georgina checked the tree first. The mommy bird was away. "Good!" she thought. "She can't complain this time." But, thanks to a naughty elf, the ball knocked into the birds' nest. A small bundle of feathers tumbled out. It was a baby bird!

Georgina spotted it and, quick as lightning, she flew up to catch him. Gently, she held him in her arms and flew back to the nest. When he was safely inside she sprinkled him with fairy dust to keep him from further harm. Just then the mommy bird came back.

"I shall tell everyone about your kindness," she said, as her baby snuggled under her feathers. "And, as you're such a good fairy, will you be baby Beak's godmother?"

"Oh, thank you! I'd be delighted!" said Georgina.

When they heard the news, the other fairies were very proud of her.

"Perhaps it's not so bad being a fairy after all," grinned Georgina, happily.

339

This is the Way the Ladies Ride

This is the way the ladies ride:
    Tri, tre, tre, tree,
    Tri, tre, tre, tree!
This is the way the ladies ride:
    Tri, tre, tre, tre, tri-tre-tre-tree!

This is the way the gentlemen ride:
    Gallop-a-trot,
    Gallop-a-trot!
This is the way the gentlemen ride:
    Gallop-a-gallop-a-trot!

This is the way the farmers ride:
    Hobbledy-hoy,
    Hobbledy-hoy!
This is the way the farmers ride:
    Hobbledy hobbledy-hoy!

This is the way the butcher boy rides,
    Tripperty-trot,
    Tripperty-trot.
Till he falls in a ditch
    With a flipperty,
    Flipperty, flop, flop, FLOP!

One Moisty Morning

One misty moisty morning,
    When cloudy was the weather,
There I met an old man
    Clothed all in leather;

Clothed all in leather,
    With cap under his chin—
How do you do, and how do you do,
    And how do you do again!

The Lion and the Unicorn

The lion and the unicorn
    Were fighting for the crown:
The lion beat the unicorn
    All round the town.
Some gave them white bread,
    Some gave them brown:
Some gave them plum-cake
    And drummed them out of town.

Old MacDonald

Old Macdonald had a farm,
   E…I…E…I…O
And on that farm he had
   some cows,
   E…I…E…I…O
With a moo-moo here,
   And a moo-moo there,
Here a moo, there a moo,
   Everywhere a moo-moo,
Old Macdonald had a farm,
   E…I…E…I…O

Old Macdonald had a farm,
   E…I…E…I…O
And on that farm he had
   some ducks,
   E…I…E…I…O
With a quack-quack here,
   And a quack-quack there,
Here a quack, there a quack,
   Everywhere a quack-quack,
Old Macdonald had a farm,
   E…I…E…I…O.

For Want of a Nail

For want of a nail, the shoe was lost;
   For want of the shoe, the horse was lost;
For want of the horse, the rider was lost;
   For want of the rider, the battle was lost;
For want of the battle, the kingdom was lost;
   And all for the want of a horseshoe nail.

A Farmyard Song

I had a cat and the cat pleased me,
   I fed my cat by yonder tree;
Cat goes fiddle-i-fee.

I had a hen and the hen pleased me,
   I fed my hen by yonder tree;
Hen goes chimmy-chuck, chimmy-chuck,
   Cat goes fiddle-i-fee.

I had a duck and the duck pleased me,
   I fed my duck by yonder tree;
Duck goes quack, quack,
   Hen goes chimmy-chuck, chimmy-chuck,
Cat goes fiddle-i-fee.

Bone Crazy

Alfie sat in his basket chewing on a large bone. Mmm! It tasted good. When he had chewed it for long enough, he took it outside to the yard, to bury it in his favorite spot, beneath the old oak tree. He didn't see next door's dog, Ferdy, watching him through a hole in the fence.

The next day, when Alfie went to dig up his bone, it was gone! He dug all around, but it was nowhere to be found. Just then, he spied a trail of muddy paw prints leading to the fence, and he realised what had happened. Alfie was too big to fit through the fence and get his bone back, so he thought of a plan, instead! Next day he buried another bone. This time, he knew Ferdy was watching him.

Later he hid and watched as Ferdy crept into the yard and started to

dig up the bone. Just then, Ferdy yelped in pain. The bone had bitten his nose! He flew across the yard and through the fence leaving the bone behind.

Alfie's friend Mole crept out from where the bone was buried. How the two friends laughed at their trick! And from then on, Ferdy always kept safely to his side of the fence!

Little Tim and his Brother Sam

Little Tim was a very lucky boy. He had a lovely home, with the nicest parents you could hope for. He had a big yard, with a swing and a soccer net in it. And growing in the yard were lots of trees that you could climb and have adventures in. Little Tim even had a nice school, which he enjoyed going to every day and where he had lots of friends. In fact, almost everything in Tim's life was nice. Everything that is apart from one thing—Tim's brother Sam.

Sam was a very naughty boy. Worse still, whenever he got into mischief—which he did almost all of the time— he managed to make it look as though someone else was to blame. And that someone was usually poor Tim!

Once Sam thought that he would put salt in the sugar bowl instead of sugar. That afternoon, Sam and Tim's parents had some friends round to visit. All the guests put salt in their cups of tea, of course, thinking it was sugar. Well, being very polite they didn't like to complain, even though their cups of tea tasted *very* strange! When Sam and Tim's parents tasted their tea, however, they guessed immediately that someone

had been playing a trick. They had to apologise to their guests and make them all fresh cups of tea. And who got the blame? Little Tim did, because Sam had sprinkled salt on Tim's bedroom floor so that their mother would think that Tim was the culprit.

Then there was the time when Sam and Tim's Aunt Jessica came to stay. She was a very nice lady, but she hated anything creepy-crawly, and as far as she was concerned that included frogs. So what did Sam do? Why, he went down to the nearby pond and got a big, green frog to put in Aunt Jessica's purse. When Aunt Jessica opened her purse to get her glasses out, there staring out of the purse at her were two froggy eyes.

"Croak!" said the frog.

"Eeek!" yelled Aunt Jessica and almost jumped out of her skin.

"I told Tim not to do it," said Sam.

Tim opened his mouth and was just about to protest his innocence when his mother said, "Tim, go to your room immediately and don't come out until you are told."

Poor Tim went to his room and had to stay there until after supper. Sam thought it was very funny.

The next day, Sam decided that he would play another prank and blame it on Tim. He went to the shed in the yard and, one by one, took out all the tools for gardening. When he thought no one was watching, he hid them all in Tim's bedroom closet. In went the spade, the fork, the watering can, the trowel—in fact, everything except the lawnmower. And the only reason that the lawnmower didn't go in was because it was too heavy to carry!

But this time, Sam's little prank was about to come unstuck, for Aunt Jessica had seen him creeping up the stairs to Tim's bedroom with the tools. She guessed immediately what Sam was up to, and who was likely to get the blame. When Sam wasn't about, she spoke to Tim. The two of them whispered to each other for a few seconds and then smiled triumphantly.

Later that day, Sam and Tim's father went to the shed to fetch some tools for gardening. Imagine his surprise when all he saw were some old flower pots and the lawnmower. He searched high and low for the tools. He looked behind the compost heap, under the steps, behind the sandpit and in the garage. And then he looked everywhere again, but they weren't anywhere to be seen.

Then he started searching in the house. He looked in all the kitchen closets, and was just looking under the stairs when something at the top of the stairs caught his eye. The handle from the big spade was sticking out of the door to Sam's bedroom. Looking rather puzzled, he went

upstairs and walked into Sam's bedroom. There, nestling neatly in the closet, were the rest of the tools.

"Sam, come up here immediately," called his father.

Sam, not realising anything was amiss, came sauntering upstairs. Suddenly he saw all the tools that he had so carefully hidden in Tim's closet now sitting in *his* closet. He was speechless.

"Right," said his father, "before you go out to play, you can take all the tools back down to the tool shed. Then you can cut the grass. Then you can dig over the flower beds, and then you can do the weeding."

Well, it took Sam hours to do all the gardening. Tim and Aunt Jessica watched from the window and clutched their sides with laughter. Sam never did find out how all the tools found their way into his bedroom, but I think you've guessed, haven't you?

Hearts, Like Doors

Hearts, like doors, will open with ease
  To very, very, little keys,
And don't forget that two of these
  Are "I thank you" and "If you please".

Mother Shuttle

Old Mother Shuttle
  Lived in a coal-scuttle
Along with her dog and her cat;
  What they ate I can't tell,
But 'tis known very well
  That not one of the party was fat.

Little Husband

I had a little husband,
  No bigger than my thumb;
I put him in a pint pot
  And there I bade him drum.
I gave him some garters
  To garter up his hose,
And a little silk handkerchief
  To wipe his pretty nose.

Rumpty-iddity

Rummpty-iddity, row, row, row,
If I had a good supper,
I could eat it now.

Willy Boy

Willy boy, Willy boy,
  Where are you going?
I will go with you,
  If that I may.
I'm going to the meadow
  To see them a-mowing,
I am going to help them
  Turn the new hay.

Two Little Dogs

Two little dogs
  Sat by the fire
Over a fender of coal-dust;
  Said one little dog
To the other little dog,
  If you don't talk, why, I must.

The Robins

A robin and a robin's son
  Once went to town to buy a bun.
They couldn't decide on a plum or plain,
  And so they went back home again.

The Merchants of London

Hey diddle dinkety, poppety, pet,
   The merchants of London they wear scarlet;
Silk in the collar and gold in the hem,
   So merrily march the merchant men.

The Dame of Dundee

There was an old woman,
   Who lived in Dundee,
And in her back garden
   There was a plum tree;
The plums they grew rotten
   Before they grew ripe,
And she sold them
   Three farthings a pint.

Christmas Eve

On Christmas Eve I turned the spit,
   I burnt my fingers, I feel it yet;
The little cock sparrow flew over the table,
   The pot began to play with the ladle.

Gingerbread Men

Smiling girls, rosy boys,
   Come and buy my little toys;
Monkeys made of gingerbread,
   And sugar horses painted red.

First

First in a carriage,
   Second in a gig,
Third on a donkey,
   And fourth on a pig.

The Wedding

Pussicat, wussicat, with a white foot,
   When is your wedding and I'll come to it.
The beer's to brew, and the bread's to bake,
   Pussicat, wussicat, don't be too late.

The Mermaid in the Pool

John and Julia were on vacation at the seaside. Their mom and dad had found an amazing house with a big swimming pool. But, best of all, their bedroom overlooked the beach. It was perfect!

The first night there was a storm. The wind howled and waves crashed over the beach, right up to the house. The children sat on the bed watching the storm outside.

In the morning, the garden furniture had blown over, there was seaweed all over the lawn and there was a mermaid swimming up and down the swimming pool! John and Julia rushed outside but, when the mermaid saw them coming, she huddled in a corner of the pool. "I'm sorry I swam into your blue pool," said the frightened mermaid.

"It's okay!" said Julia gently. "We didn't mean to frighten you. We just wanted to meet you. We've never seen a mermaid before."

"My name is Marina," said the mermaid. "I was playing in the sea with my friend Blue the dolphin, when the storm began. A huge wave washed me in, and now I'm stranded, and Blue is missing!"

"We'll help you look for Blue," said Julia at once. "We might be able to see your friend from our bedroom window."

When their mom and dad were safely out of the way, John and Julia found a wheelbarrow and wheeled Marina into the house. "I've only had sky over my head," said Marina. "The house won't fall down will it?"

"Of course not," smiled John. They showed Marina all sorts of things she had never seen before. She thought the moving pictures on the television were weird. She thought Julia's teddy bear was wonderful, and that beds were the silliest things she had ever seen! But, although they looked out of the window, there was no sign of Blue the dolphin in the sea.

"I have to go home soon!" Marina said sadly. "I can't stay out of the water for long, and I must find Blue. If only I hadn't lost my shell horn in the storm I could call him."

"We'll take you down to the sea," said John. "And help you look for your shell," said Julia.

They lifted Marina back into the wheelbarrow and pushed her down to the beach. They spent the rest of the day searching for Marina's shell along the seashore. Suddenly, Julia spotted a large shell half buried in the sand. John found a stick and dug it out.

"It's my shell!" cried Marina. They washed off the sand and Marina blew into it. The most beautiful sound drifted out across the waves and, straight away, there was an answering call! Far out to sea, they saw a streak of blue-gray leaping high over the waves, swimming towards them. It was Blue the dolphin!

Marina gave a cry of joy and swam to meet him. She flung her arms round his neck and hugged him. Then she called out to the watching children. "Thank you both for helping me."

"See you next year!" called John and Julia.

And they watched as Marina and Blue swam swiftly and smoothly together, back out to sea.

Patch on Patrol

Early one morning, Farmer Sam was driving his tractor, when he saw something moving at the side of the road. He stopped the tractor and jumped down to take a look. "Well, well," said Sam. "What are you doing here?"

A small puppy tried to wag his tail. He was shivering and crying. Sam gently picked up the puppy, brushed away the dirt and leaves and tucked him inside his warm jacket. "I'd better get you to Haven Farm Animal Hospital," he said.

At the animal hospital, the Haven family took the puppy from Farmer Sam, promising to look after him. "What a scruffy mess!" said Dad. "I'm sure a bath and some good food will make him feel much better." So, Sally and Joe decided to call the puppy Scruff. After a bath, they put him in a basket by the fire. "Scruff's so friendly!" said Sally. "I'm sure he must have a family, somewhere. They'll be missing him so much."

"Let's make a poster," said Joe. "We can put it up in the town, when we go shopping with Mom."

Later that day, Joe and Sally pinned their poster up in the town.

Mom followed with Scruff on a lead. Scruff was
so excited that he ran round and round, getting
Mom in such a tangle! "Scruff's
going to be so good at rounding
up people!" said Joe, laughing.

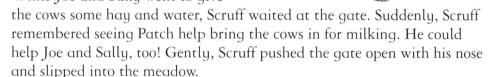

Back at the farm, Sally
and Joe took Scruff with
them so that he would get
used to all the other animals.
While Joe and Sally went to give
the cows some hay and water, Scruff waited at the gate. Suddenly, Scruff
remembered seeing Patch help bring the cows in for milking. He could
help Joe and Sally, too! Gently, Scruff pushed the gate open with his nose
and slipped into the meadow.

Scruff barked and ran round the meadow, the same way he had seen
Patch round up the sheep! The cows ran in every direction, until Marigold,
the oldest cow, led them all out of the field towards the milking shed.
"No, Scruff, no!" wailed Joe and Sally. "It's not milking time yet!" But
Scruff, pleased to have helped, just wagged his tail, which, like the rest of
him, was covered in mud, grass and cow dung!

Luckily, Patch heard the cows coming up the lane and knew just what
to do. He stopped Marigold before she reached the milking shed and
barked at her to go back to the
meadow. Mooing loudly, Marigold
turned around and all the other cows
followed her back. "Good dog, Patch!"
said Sally. "As for you, Scruff, you'll
have to have a bath. You stink!"

Scruff lay in the warm sun with
Patch, while everybody had lunch.

Then he left Patch snoozing and trotted off to explore the farm. Patch opened one eye and sighed. He would have to follow Scruff to make sure he didn't get into any more trouble!

Scruff decided to look in the stables. There, he spotted Tabby the cat, asleep on top of the hay. Scruff wanted to say hello, so he leapt on to the hay, barking with excitement. Tabby woke with a fright and was so alarmed that she ran away into Old Major's stall. Chasing after her, Scruff came right up against Old Major's huge back feet. Thump! The grumpy horse knocked Scruff out of the way. The puppy was bowled over and over, until he landed behind some hay bales. Just then, Patch arrived. He gently nudged Scruff and knew that he had to get help so he ran back to the farmhouse to find Joe and Sally.

"Hey, Patch," said Joe, as Patch appeared in the kitchen doorway, barking, "what's the matter?"

"Where's Scruff, Patch?" asked Sally, looking around for the puppy. Patch just barked all the more.

"Mom!" said Joe. "Something's wrong!" Joe, Sally and Mom followed Patch to the stables, where Scruff was lying in the hay.

"Look! Poor Scruff's hurt!" cried Sally. Mom knelt beside Scruff and gently examined him.

"He's hurt his leg," she said. "He must have gone too near Old Major. We'll take him to the surgery." Joe and Sally carefully placed the puppy into Mom's apron and took him to Dad. Dad had a good look at Scruff, while Sally, Joe and Patch watched.

"How is he?" asked Joe.

"Well, his leg is broken, I'm afraid," said Dad. "It should mend quite quickly, but he won't be able to run around for a while."

"I expect Patch and the other animals will be pleased about that!" laughed Sally.

A few days later, Dad had good news for them all. "Scruff's owners have just called!" he told them. "They saw your poster and they're coming to collect him." Joe and Sally didn't want to lose Scruff, but they knew that the puppy should be back with his family.

"I hope they are nice," whispered Sally to Joe. She needn't have worried! That afternoon, a little boy and his mom came to Haven Farm.

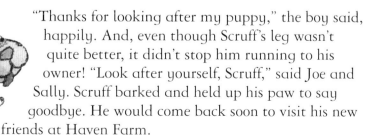

"Thanks for looking after my puppy," the boy said, happily. And, even though Scruff's leg wasn't quite better, it didn't stop him running to his owner! "Look after yourself, Scruff," said Joe and Sally. Scruff barked and held up his paw to say goodbye. He would come back soon to visit his new friends at Haven Farm.

Who Can Save the Chicks?

One morning on Windy Farm, three naughty chicks escaped from their hen house and waddled into the farmyard. "Yippeeeeee!" they cheeped, noisily. "I know that Mommy said we weren't allowed outside the hen house by ourselves," cheeped Chalky Chick, "but there's nothing to do inside! Let's go to the river and play."

"That's a great idea!" cried the other chicks. What fun the chicks had, down by the river. But, as the chicks had fun, they didn't realised that danger was nearby!

Wicked Fox was hiding behind the tree. "Lunch!" he murmured. "I'm going to get them!" Luckily, up in the tree, Owl had woken and spotting Fox he flew off to the farm, for help. But everyone was out searching for the missing chicks. Only Pig was left.

"Quickly," cried Owl to Pig. "Fox is going to eat the chicks!" Pig got up and ran after Owl, as fast as he could. Once Pig got moving, there was no stopping him! And, as he staggered to the river, he crashed into that nasty fox, tossing him into the water with a big, loud SPLASH!

"Everyone was worried about you," said Pig to the little chicks, sternly.

"We're sorry!" cheeped the chicks. "We won't do it again—but getting wet was fun!" And Pig and the chicks dripped all the way back home!

It's Not Fair!

"I want to swim with the duckling," said Kitten to Mother Cat, as they walked past the pond.

"You can't," Mother Cat told her. "Your fur isn't waterproof."

"I want to roll in the mud with the piglets," said Kitten, when they walked past the pigsty.

"You can't," Mother Cat told her. "Your long fur will get knotted and matted with mud."

"I want to fly with the baby birds," said Kitten to Mother Cat, as she tried to climb where baby birds were learning to fly.

"You can't," Mother Cat told her. "You have fur, not feathers and you haven't got wings. Kittens aren't meant to fly."

"It's not fair!" shouted Kitten. "Kittens don't have any fun!"

Later, Kitten curled up on a rug by the kitchen fire, with a saucer of milk.

"I want to sleep by the fire," said Duckling, standing at the door.

"And I want to lie on a rug," said Piglet, trotting past the door.

"And I want to drink a saucer of milk, said a Baby Bird as he flew past.

"It's not fair!" shouted Duckling, Piglet and Baby Bird as Mother Cat shooed them away.

"Oh yes, it is!" mewed Kitten, smiling!

Tough Ted Loses his Growl

The alarm clock started to ring and Katie jumped out of bed, bursting with energy. Tough Ted opened one sleepy eye (which was all he could do, as the other one had fallen off years ago) and stretched out his paws.

"Another morning," he yawned. "I don't suppose it will be a good one."

Tough Ted was a very old bear. He had belonged to Katie's mum when she was young. He had been a smart teddy then, and happy, but now he was in a sorry state and was always grumpy. He was the oldest of the toys and had been through some tough times. The others loved him, but they were fed up with his constant moaning and groaning.

"When is this bed going to be made? I can't get comfortable with all these covers thrown back!" he complained. "And they should pull that blind down, the sun's shining straight into my eye," he grumbled. "Talking of which, it's about time they gave me a new one," he moaned. He carried on growling all morning.

"If he doesn't stop complaining soon I'm going to stuff my hat in his mouth," whispered Soldier to Clown, as they sat nearby on the shelf.

"Not if I put my juggling balls in there first!" said Clown. All the toys giggled.

"It's about time we taught him a lesson," said Rag Doll.

"But what can we do to stop him moaning?" said Soldier.

"What about sticking a band-aid over his mouth while he's asleep?" twittered Owl, who was always wise.

"That's a great idea, Owl!" said Rag Doll, and everyone agreed.

So that night, Rag Doll fetched a band-aid from the bathroom cabinet, and stuck it firmly over Tough Ted's mouth while he was asleep. All the toys were delighted—peace and quiet at last!

The next morning the alarm clock went off and Katie went into the bathroom. Tough Ted opened his eye and was just about to moan that the alarm was still ringing, when he realised he could not open his mouth! He pulled and stretched and twisted his face as hard as he could, but he could not get his mouth to open. Then he noticed that all the toys were

watching him. When he looked and saw the band-aid in the mirror he was furious! He ripped it off and turned to face the other toys angrily.

"Who did this?" he bellowed. "When I find out who it was, there'll be trouble, growwwll! Have you no respect for an old bear?" He went on and on and on. He grew red in the face, and looked terribly cross. All the toys became quite scared.

Then, as he was growling at the top of his voice, a funny thing happened. His voice began to crack. He tried to clear his throat, but it was no use. No matter how hard he tried, he could not make a sound. He had lost his voice completely!

"Well it serves you right!" said Rag Doll. "All you do is moan, moan, moan, and we're tired of listening to you. We put the band-aid on your mouth to teach you a lesson. But now you've moaned so much that you've made yourself lose your voice completely."

With that, a big tear rolled down Tough Ted's cheek. He was not so tough after all. He hadn't realised that he moaned so much, and he felt very sorry.

Rag Doll did not like seeing Tough Ted so sad. All the toys felt a bit guilty for what they had done.

"I'll go and get some honey from the kitchen," said Rag Doll. "It will soothe your throat. But you must promise not to start moaning again."

After Rag Doll had given Tough Ted a spoonful of honey, he whispered, "I'm sorry. I promise I'll try not to moan any more. I didn't realise I'd become such a grumpy old bear."

With that, all the toys gave Tough Ted a hug and Rag Doll gave him some more honey.

Since then Tough Ted has tried really hard not to moan. But, whenever he does, he thinks about the band-aid and quickly stops himself before anyone hears! And the rest of the toys do their best to look after him and keep him happy.

Where's Wanda?

Sally was worried. Wanda, her cat, was getting fat. She was behaving very strangely, too. She wouldn't go in her basket. "She must be ill," Sally told her mommy. "Her tummy's all swollen, and she hasn't slept in her basket for days."

"Don't worry," said Mommy, giving Sally a hug. "If she's not better in the morning, we'll take her to the vet."

"Sssh!" whispered Sally. "You know how much Wanda hates the V-E-T." But it was too late, Wanda had already gone.

Sally and her mommy couldn't find Wanda anywhere. She didn't even come running when they left out a saucer of milk. Wanda was still missing the following morning.

"She must have heard us talking about the vet," said Sally, as they searched around the house. "Perhaps she's hiding in the yard," she said.

They looked in the flowerbed, under the hedge, and up the tree. But all they found there were the birds. "Sometimes she sunbathes in the vegetable patch," said Sally. But the only animal there was a fluffy rabbit.

"Wanda!" called Mommy, looking in the shed. Wanda often liked sleeping in there. Today all they found there were mice.

"Maybe she's been locked in the garage," said Sally.

They looked around the car. They looked in the car. They even looked under it. But all they found there were spiders.

Wanda was nowhere around the house or yard, so Mommy took Sally  to look in the park. "Here, Wanda!" called Sally. But all they found there were dogs. Wanda hated dogs, so she wouldn't be there.

On the way home, Sally even sat on Mommy's shoulders so that she could look on top of people's garages and sheds. "She must have run away," cried Sally. "We're never going to find her."

But Mommy had an idea. She helped Sally to draw some pictures of Wanda. Then they wrote MISSING and their telephone number on the pictures. They posted the leaflets through all the letterboxes in the street.

In the afternoon Mrs Jones from next door popped her head over the hedge. "Come and see what I've found in my laundry basket," smiled Mrs Jones. Sally and her mommy rushed next door at once. When Sally saw what Mrs Jones had in her laundry basket she couldn't believe her eyes.

There, sitting amongst the washing, was Wanda. She looked very slim and very proud. And beside her lay five tiny kittens. They were so young that their eyes were still closed. Wanda hadn't been ill after all. She'd been expecting kittens!

Mrs Jones said that they could keep the basket until Wanda had finished with it. So Mommy carried the new family home as Sally skipped beside her.

Sally was so excited. She just couldn't wait to tell people how they'd gone searching for one cat and found six!

The Disappearing Trick

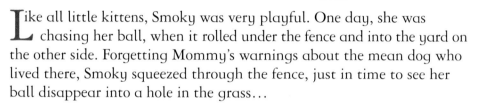

Like all little kittens, Smoky was very playful. One day, she was chasing her ball, when it rolled under the fence and into the yard on the other side. Forgetting Mommy's warnings about the mean dog who lived there, Smoky squeezed through the fence, just in time to see her ball disappear into a hole in the grass...

Smoky looked down into the hole, but it was very deep and there was no sign of the ball. Just then, she heard a low growl, and turned to see an angry dog snarling at her.

In a flash, she scrambled into the hole, with the dog's sharp teeth snapping at her heels. She squeezed down a long tunnel and into a little room at the bottom.

"Hello!" said Rabbit, handing Smoky the ball. "You must be looking for this!"

Smoky was amazed to find she was in Rabbit's burrow. She told him about the angry dog. "Don't worry," said Rabbit, "we'll trick him!"

He dug a new tunnel and in no time they were back in Smoky's yard.

"Over here!" Rabbit called through the fence to the poor dog still guarding the hole! How the two friends laughed to see the puzzled look on his face.

The Chocolate Soldier

In the window of Mrs Brown's candy store there stood a chocolate soldier. He had chocolate ears and eyebrows and a curly chocolate mustache of which he was particularly proud. But best of all he loved his shiny foil uniform with its braid on the shoulders, and smart red stripes down each leg. All day long the chocolate soldier stood to attention on a shelf in the window, staring straight ahead into the street. Standing next to him on the shelf were more chocolate soldiers, some lollipops, some sugar mice and a twist of licorice bootlaces.

It was summer time and the sun shone through the window of the candy store. At first the chocolate soldier felt pleasantly warm; then he started to feel uncomfortably hot. Next he began to feel most peculiar indeed. His chocolate mustache was wilting and his arms were dripping. Soon he was completely melted and, before he knew it, he had slipped out through a hole in his silver foil shoe and was pouring off the shelf and out into the street.

Down the street he poured.

"Stop! Help me!" he shouted, but nobody could hear his cries.

Now he could hear the sound of gushing water and, to his horror, he could see he was heading for a stream at the bottom of the street.

"Help me! I can't swim! I'm going to drown!" the chocolate soldier cried as he plunged into the cold, running water. But now something very strange was happening—he found he could swim quite easily. He looked round and saw that he had a chocolate tail covered in scales. Then he looked at his arms, but there was a pair of fins instead. The cold water had hardened him into the shape of a chocolate fish!

The water carried the chocolate soldier until the stream broadened out and became a river. He realised that he would soon be carried out to sea.

"Whatever shall I do?" wondered the chocolate soldier. "I'm sure to get eaten by a bigger fish or maybe even a shark!" He tried to turn around and swim against the river's flow but it was no good. The current swept him away down river again.

Soon he could see the waves on the shore. He smelt the sea air and tasted the salt in the water. Now he found himself bobbing up and down on the sea. He could see a boat not far away and then all of a sudden he felt a net closing around him. He struggled to get out, but the net only tightened and soon he felt himself being hauled out of the water and landed with a "thwack!" on the deck among a pile of fish. The smell was awful, and the chocolate soldier was quite relieved when he felt the boat being rowed towards the shore.

"I'll hop over the side as soon as we land and run away," he thought, quite forgetting that he had no legs but only a fish's tail.

But there was no chance of escape. As soon as the boat reached the shore, he and all the other fish were flung into buckets and lifted into a truck. The truck stopped outside a diner and a man carried the buckets inside, where it smelt of burgers and fresh fries. The chocolate soldier found himself being lifted up with a lot of other fish in a huge metal basket. He looked down and saw a terrible sight below. They were heading for a vat of boiling oil! At that very moment he felt very peculiar once again. His scales melted, his tail drooped and he felt himself slide through the holes in the basket and into the pocket of a man's apron.

The chocolate soldier lay in the corner of the pocket while the man worked in the diner. Then the man went home, with the chocolate soldier bouncing up and down in the apron pocket as the man walked along. Soon they arrived at the man's house. He reached into his pocket.

"Look what I've found," he said to his small son. "A coin. Here, you can have it—but don't spend it all at once!" he said, chuckling to himself. The chocolate soldier felt himself being passed from one hand to another.

"So now I've become a chocolate coin," he thought. "And I'm going to be eaten!" But to his surprise he was slipped into the boy's pocket.

The chocolate soldier felt himself bouncing up and down as the boy ran up the street and into a store. The chocolate soldier peeped out and to his astonishment saw that he was back in Mrs Brown's candy store. The boy believed he was a real coin and was going to try and spend him!

The chocolate soldier called out to his soldier friends in the window,

THE CHOCOLATE SOLDIER

"Pssst! It's me! Help me!" One of the soldiers looked down, but all he could see was a chocolate coin sticking out of the boy's pocket. Then he recognised the voice.

"I'm a chocolate soldier too, but I've been turned into a coin. Help!" cried the chocolate soldier.

"Just leave it to me," replied the soldier on the shelf. "Don't worry, we'll have you out of there in a flash!"

The word was passed along and one of the sugar mice chewed off a length of licorice bootlace. Then the soldier lowered the lace into the boy's pocket, where it stuck to the chocolate coin. Carefully the soldiers hauled the coin up on to the shelf. The chocolate soldier was delighted to find his foil uniform was still there on the shelf, just where it had been before. All the effort of getting on to the shelf had made him quite warm, and he found he could slip quite easily back through the hole in the shoe and into his uniform again.

"I'd like a chocolate soldier," said the boy to Mrs Brown. But when he reached in his pocket the coin had gone.

"Never mind," said kind Mrs Brown. "You can have one anyway." She reached into the window and took down a soldier from the end of the row and gave it to the boy. And as for our chocolate soldier? In the cool of the night he turned back into a smart-looking soldier again.

Town Mouse and Country Mouse

Once there was a roly-poly, wiggly-whiskered mouse, who lived in a snug little nest under an oak tree. Country Mouse loved his home. He had plenty of acorns, nuts and berries to eat and a warm and cozy straw bed to sleep in. Squirrel and Robin, who lived in the oak tree, were the best neighbors he could ever wish for.

One day, Country Mouse had a surprise. His cousin, Town Mouse, came to visit from the Big City. Town Mouse was sleek and slender, with a smooth, shiny coat. His whiskers were smart and elegant. Country Mouse felt a little ordinary beside him. But he didn't mind. All he wanted to do was make Town Mouse feel welcome. "Are you hungry, Cousin?" he said. "Come and have some supper!"

But Town Mouse didn't like the acorns and blackberries that Country Mouse gave him to eat. They were tough and sour. And Town Mouse thought his cousin's friends were boring. The straw bed that he slept in that night was so rough and scratchy that he didn't sleep a wink!

TOWN MOUSE AND COUNTRY MOUSE

Next day, Town Mouse said, "Come to the Big City with me, Cousin. It's so much more exciting than the country! I live in a grand house, eat delicious food and have exciting adventures. Come with me and see what you've been missing!" It sounded so wonderful, Country Mouse couldn't resist it. Saying goodbye to his friends, the cousins set off for the city.

When they arrived in the Big City, Country Mouse was frightened. It was so noisy— horns blared and wheels clattered all around them. Huge trucks roared and rumbled down the street and the smelly, smoky air made them choke and cough. And there were dogs *everywhere*!

At last, they arrived safely at Town Mouse's house. It was very grand, just as Town Mouse had said. But it was *so* big! Country Mouse was afraid that he would get lost!

"Don't worry," said Town Mouse to Country Mouse. "You'll soon learn your way around the house. For now, just stay close to me. I'm starving—let's go and have a snack." Country Mouse was hungry, too, so he followed his cousin to the kitchen.

Country Mouse had never seen so much delicious food—there were plates full of fruit, nuts, cheese and cakes.

He and his cousin ate and ate and ate! But Country Mouse wasn't used to this sort of rich food. Before he knew it, his tummy was aching.

Suddenly, a huge woman came into the room. "Eek! Mice!" she screamed. She grabbed a big broom and began to swat the mice, who scampered off as fast as they could.

As the two mice scurried across the floor, Country Mouse thought things couldn't possibly get worse. But how wrong he was! A big cat suddenly sprang out from behind a chair! With a loud MEEOOWW, he pounced on the two little mice. Country Mouse had never been so frightened. He darted and dashed as fast as his aching tummy would let him. The two mice jumped through a mousehole and were safe at last in Town Mouse's house.

"Phew! I think we've done enough for one day," said Town

Mouse, when they had caught their breath. "Let's get some sleep," he said, with a yawn. "I'll show you the rest of the house in the morning." Country Mouse curled up in the hard little bed. But he was too frightened and unhappy to sleep. As he listened to his cousin snore, he tried hard not to cry.

Next morning, Town Mouse was ready for more adventures, but Country Mouse had had more than enough.

"Thank you for inviting me," he told his cousin, "but I have seen all I want to see of the Big City. It is too big and noisy and dirty—and too full of danger for me. I want to go back to my quiet, peaceful home in the country."

So, Country Mouse went back to his snug, cozy home under the oak tree. He had never been so happy to see his friends—and they wanted to hear all about his adventures. Country Mouse was pleased to tell them everything that had happened in the Big City—but he *never, ever* went back there again!

Such a Pickle!

Old MacDonald has quite a few pigs on his farm. He has two that are favorites—Percy, and the eldest one, Jonathan Jakes Jermington Jollop.

Jonathan Jakes Jermington Jollop is the pig's birth name, but now he is called something much less grand! This is the story of how he got his new name.

When Jonathan Jakes Jermington Jollop was a piglet, he somehow got the idea that he was much better than all the other animals that lived on the farm. It was partly because he had such a long name, and partly because Old MacDonald liked to come and chat to him.

"I don't know what's the matter with that young pig," clucked Henrietta the hen. "I said hello to him this morning, and he didn't say a word. He just put his nose in the air and trotted off."

"He did the very same to me," neighed Old George the horse.

Soon there wasn't an animal left on the farm who had a good word to say about Jonathan Jakes Jermington Jollop—and the piglet only had himself to blame!

So, when Jonathan Jakes Jermington Jollop saw Henry the rooster standing on the henhouse roof, and he decided to climb on to the roof of his pen, that is why no one tried to stop him.

Now, pigs are not well-known for their climbing skills, but this didn't stop Jonathan Jakes Jermington Jollop! He scrabbled and scrambled, puffed and panted, and eventually the young pig found himself perched rather uncomfortably on the top of his pen.

He soon realised that he had a very big problem. Getting up had not been easy, but he could see that getting down was going to be practically impossible—and he discovered that he was scared of heights!

Before long, there was a crowd around the pigpen. There was mooing and baaing, neighing and clucking, as they looked at the panicking pig on the roof.

"How did that silly piglet get into such a pickle?" Annabel the cow mooed.

"What a ridiculous place for a piglet to sit," clucked Henrietta the hen. "That's a place for hens not piglets!"

"Hey, Pickle Piglet!" quacked Doris the duck. "What are you doing up there, and how are you going to get down?" she asked.

"I've been really silly," said Jonathan Jakes Jermington Jollop, looking very upset. "Please help me!"

With a laugh, Old George picked him up by his tail and plonked him on the floor.

Jonathan Jakes Jermington Jollop looked very relieved to have all four trotters on firm ground again, and he smiled happily at the other farm animals as they crowded round him.

Jonathan Jakes Jermington Jollop never put on airs and graces again, and no one let him forget his climbing adventure. From that day on, Jonathan Jakes Jermington Jollop was forever known as Pickles the pig!

At the Monster Café

Down at the Monster Café there are sights you just would not believe! Monsters love their food, their portions are huge and the colors are scary. As for the ingredients, it might be better not to know, as you will see!

A monster stew is a grisly mixture of turnip tops and vile black drops, and monsters have spaghetti hoops with licorice loops! They eat brown rats' tails, slugs and snails, and add lots of little flies for decoration.

As for the favorite monster drink—it is lime green, mauve and pink, and made with peas and dead gnat's knees. They say that this goes particularly well with the favorite monster candies. These are made of dragons' feet, with sugared claws and chocolate paws—sounds really gruesome doesn't it?

Monster snacks start to bubble when you take off the wrapper. They are made from tar and bits of car, which sounds more like torture than a treat! Fortunately most monsters have very large, sharp teeth so they can munch away merrily on their snacks without breaking them.

The most frightening part of the monster menu is the price list—it is very expensive to eat at the Monster Café. But to a monster it is a real treat. Will you be saving up for a visit?

Cooking
up a
Storm

Wizards love to cook. They have a huge cauldron for mixing their magic potions, which means they also have all they need to create huge and wonderful stews for their wizard friends.

There is a difference between what you or I might think of as a stew, and what a stew might be to a wizard. For instance, we can go to a local shop to buy our ingredients whereas a wizard might go down to his local pond! The favorite wizard stew is called Storm and, when you know what goes in it, you will understand why!

First the wizard has to put a handful of cat's whiskers into a cauldron of boiling dirty pond water. Then he adds the tails from three young pups, a big ladle of eyeballs and two cups of froggy slime. This is stirred slowly for seventeen minutes before adding giant fireworks, a bunch of old tin cans, a pair of cymbals and a big bass drum. Then the windows start to shake and the sky darkens—here comes the storm that goes with the stew! As it rains cats and dogs, and a shower of nasty frogs, the stew is ready. The wizard has cooked up a storm!